D1571836

Drinking Careers

Occupations,
Drinking Habits,
and Drinking Problems

Drinking
Careers

Occupations,
Drinking Habits,
and Drinking Problems

MARTIN A. PLANT

TAVISTOCK
PUBLICATIONS

LIBRARY OF
WINE INSTITUTE

First published in 1979
by Tavistock Publications Limited
11 New Fetter Lane, London EC4P 4EE
© 1979 Martin A. Plant
Typeset by Red Lion Setters, London
and printed in Great Britain at the
University Press, Cambridge

ISBN 0 422 76590 2

This book is dedicated to Emma Judith Plant,
born November 12th, 1978

'You want to know why men drink? The working man has few pleasures, apart from sex. I'm too old for that now, so all I really enjoy is a good drink. I used to drink a lot. Now I only drink on Saturdays. I get drunk every weekend. I always drink to get drunk. It's my only real pleasure. I get drunk a lot easier than I used to. Once I worked in the Shetlands. All the people there I stayed with or worked with liked "the drink". I used to drink one or two bottles of whisky every day.'

(Retired brewery worker)

Contents

Figures and tables

x *Drinking Careers*

Tables

Acknowledgements

The planning, execution, and reporting of the work described in this book were helped by a large number of people. While the companies participating in this study cannot be named, I am exceedingly grateful to the managements, trade unions, and workers for their co-operation and courtesy and for countless cups of coffee. I am grateful for help and advice from the Brewers' Society and the Scotch Whisky Association in devising this research in the first place. All of the work reported hereafter was carried out while I was a member of the Medical Research Council Unit for Epidemiological Studies in Psychiatry, Edinburgh. I am particularly indebted to Dr Norman Kreitman, Mr John Duffy, Dr Jonathan Chick, and to other colleagues in that Unit for their constructive criticism and encouragement. I am also grateful to Dr Griffith Edwards, Dr Paul Gwinner, Dr Brian Hore, Dr Robin Murray, Dr Keith Rix, and Mr Bill Saunders, all of whom drew my attention to studies of their own and other people's which were invaluable to this research. Dr David Robinson read the original design for, and the initial draft of, this book and recommended sensible modifications. My wife, Moira, in addition to all her usual help and support, suggested numerous improvements to the original text while undergoing the stresses and nausea of pregnancy. The typing was shared efficiently by Mrs Valerie Mackenzie, Mrs Wilma Seaton and Mrs Caroline Urquhart, who between them managed to read my writing. The faults are, needless to say, my own.

Some of the work in this book has appeared in journals, though the presentation and analysis adopted here diverges from previous publications. Acknowledgements of copyright and thanks for permission to cite are made to the following:

British Journal of Addiction for
Plant, M.A. (1977) Alcoholism and Occupation: A review, 72: 309-16.
International Journal of the Addictions for
Plant, M.A. (1978) Occupation and Alcoholism: Cause or effect? A Controlled Study of Recruits to the Drink Trade, 13: 605-26.

Martin Plant

Introduction

The central concern of this book is the relationship between an individual's drinking habits and social setting. The way in which a person drinks or does not drink is influenced by age, sex, religion, nationality, and possibly by personality and heredity. In spite of this, people's drinking habits frequently and, sometimes, dramatically change, as do their experiences of the problems which, if extreme or numerous enough, are sometimes called 'alcoholism'.

This book is an empirical, rather than a theoretical, work. It does not attempt to expound a general theory of either 'normal' or 'deviant' drinking. Drinking habits and alcohol-related problems are discussed in relation to a follow-up study of a cohort of Scottish male manual workers in 'high-' and 'low-risk' occupational settings. It is clearly shown that an individual may move into and out of 'problem drinking', and that very often this appears to be explained by the social group to which that person currently belongs. Many alcohol-related problems are purely temporary and some 'problem drinkers' resolve their difficulties for themselves without recourse either to specialized treatment or to professional advice.

Chapter 1 summarizes the properties of the drug alcohol, and describes some of the social aspects of drinking behaviour. 'Alcoholism' is defined and it is suggested that it is not a clear-cut disease so much as the end of a continuum of alcohol-related problems.

Chapter 2 reviews the extensive literature indicating that some occupational groups have especially high rates of heavy drinking and alcohol-related problems. Possible explanations for this fact are suggested.

Chapter 3 laments the inadequacy of information about drinking habits and 'alcoholism'. The reader is warned not to place excessive faith in poor data.

Chapter 4 describes the aims, design, and methods employed in a follow-up study of 150 men recruited into alcohol production and 150 men in 'lower-risk' jobs.

Chapters 5 to 7 describe the biographical characteristics, drinking habits, and alcohol-related problems of these 300 men upon entry into their new jobs and as they remain in them, become unemployed, or move into different work situations.

Chapter 8 reviews the empirical and theoretical implications of the results of this study and discusses the ways in which drinking habits and alcohol-related problems emerge and change.

1 Alcohol, drinking, and drinking problems

Virtually every social group uses some substance or other as a way of achieving a changed state of consciousness, of relaxing, or of getting 'high'. The particular substances chosen have been largely matters of botanical convenience: tobacco for North American Indians, coca for those in South America, cannabis for the Vietnamese. The popularity of alcohol stems largely from its relative ease of production in so many different areas. Himalayan villagers can ferment it from rice, Italians from the grape, and Scots from barley.

Alcohol is firmly established as the major relaxant and social drug of Western society. Its production is a major source of employment and of tax revenue. Its consumption is a major part of many, if not most, social occasions. Alcohol is much more than just a beverage like tea or coffee. It is an important symbol of hospitality and a widely relied upon catalyst for conviviality. Nevertheless, alcohol is a drug which can produce dependence and is misused tragically by a minority of those who drink it (Royal College of Psychiatrists 1979; Grant and Gwinner 1979).

In this chapter the properties of alcohol as a drug are described briefly. Some of the social aspects of drinking are examined including how young people learn about drinking and how drinking habits vary between different social groups. Finally, an account is given of alcohol-related problems, popularly, and often inaccurately, referred to as 'alcoholism'.

Alcohol as a drug

Alcohol has been called 'man's oldest drug' (Einstein 1975: 75). Apart from its commonplace use as a source of enjoyment it has a long record of use as a medicine, a food, part of religious ritual, even as the elixir of life. The word alcohol is derived from the Arabic Al-Koh'l which is antimony sulphide, a powder used in the East for darkening eyebrows and eyelashes. Alcoholic beverages have been used since prehistory, though it is possible that Arabian chemists produced the first alcohol distilled from wine. There are many local names for alcoholic drinks. Its historical esteem is indicated by the fact that it has been called *aqua vitae*, the water of life.

There are many different chemicals called alcohol. The one that concerns us is *ethyl alcohol*. Only this has the effects generally required of alcohol and is safe to drink. Ethyl alcohol is a compound of carbon, hydrogen, and oxygen. It is a clear liquid with an astringent taste and little smell of its own. The well-known smell on the drinker's breath is usually caused by other ingredients apart from alcohol. Ethyl alcohol burns with a pale blue non-luminous flame. Its boiling point is less than that of water, at 78° centigrade, and its freezing point is low, which is why it is often used in thermometers and compasses.

Alcoholic drinks have long been subject to taxation. Usually the amount of ethyl alcohol in a specific beverage has been an important consideration in establishing tax levels. Duty has been calculated in relation to the so-called 'proof'. Originally gunpowder was soaked with the beverage under test or 'proving'. If, when ignited, the powder flashed, the spirit was 'over-proof'. If it did not, it was 'under-proof'. More sophisticated measurement techniques have enabled the percentage of ethyl alcohol in a beverage to be established fairly accurately. The proof of an alcoholic drink is now stated as a specific number. Pure alcohol is 200 proof, but is in practice about 189 proof (since it becomes diluted by moisture in the air). Most British beers contain about 4 per cent of ethyl alcohol. Wines generally range from 12 to 16 per cent and spirits contain roughly 50 per cent, although, confusingly, these are described as 85 to 100 proof (i.e. about half as strong as pure ethyl alcohol which is 180 to 200 proof).

The drug effects of alcohol depend not upon the specific type of drink, be it beer, wine, or spirits, but upon the quantity of ethyl alcohol consumed. A rough guide is that a pint of beer is similar in alcohol content (and effects) to either two normal measures of spirits or to two glasses of wine. There is no evidence that any of the other ingredients of alcoholic drinks, known as congeners, have any important effects.

Alcohol is passed from the stomach and intestines into the bloodstream and is diffused through the tissues of the body. It is broken down and disposed of by oxidation, mainly by the liver. This turns it into carbon dioxide and water. Different people take different amounts of time to oxidize any given amount of alcohol. Large people are less affected by alcohol, and dispose of it more quickly, than smaller people. The speed of oxidation is not affected by the quantity of alcohol consumed, so that someone who has drunk a lot will take longer to return to normal than someone who has drunk much less.

Alcohol mainly affects the nervous system and is a *depressant*, slowing down all of its activities. This is, of course, contrary to the popular belief that alcohol is a stimulant that makes people lively and extroverted. While alcohol depresses the general level of activity, it also reduces the level of a person's inhibitions. It thereby makes people feel more relaxed, and provides the 'Dutch courage' for which it is so widely used:

> 'Wi tippeny [ale] we fear nae evil
> Wi usquebae [whisky], we'll face the devil.'
> (Robert Burns)

One major problem is that alcohol on the one hand makes people feel more confident and capable, while on the other hand it is in fact slowing them down. A commonplace example of this paradox is the ill-informed driver who insists that he is better able to drive after a drink or two. In fact, his abilities are impaired, even though his self-confidence is unrealistically inflated.

The reduction of inhibitions caused by alcohol is in the main socially desirable and beneficial. A drink or two gets a party going, helps people to relax, to flirt, and to unwind. Sometimes drinking can lead to less positive actions. A very high proportion of crimes of violence are committed under the influence of alcohol, suggesting that not all inhibitions are bad ones.

In addition to its depressant effects on the nervous system, alcohol may increase heart rate slightly and will increase the flow of blood to the skin. This leads to a 'flushing' effect. One consequence of this is that core body temperature is reduced. It is an important rule of first aid *never* to give alcohol to people who are injured, or suffering from exposure, because it cools them down. During wartime men have been rescued alive from the sea only to expire after being dosed with 'warming' rum. Drinking increases the rate of urination, partly because of increased fluid consumption and partly through affecting the pituitary gland.

Alcohol is also a food:

'As a provider of calories it must, in Britain, be one of the most expensive, and certainly the most extensively taxed. It is a carbohydrate and because of its rapid absorption from the stomach it is a quick source of energy. However, this energy cannot be used efficiently because of the inco-ordinating and intoxicating effects of alcohol. Only the self-deceiving can believe they are doing something dietetically useful by drinking, except for stimulating the appetite.'

(Kessel and Walton 1974: 25)

Many of the problems connected with alcohol, which are referred to later in this chapter, stem from the fact that its possible dangers are often not readily apparent. In the short term, reduced inhibitions, together with sluggish behaviour, combine to damage a person's judgement. The longer-term dangers are also not obvious. Alcohol is a drug of dependence. People can become addicted to it. Unlike some other drugs, such as heroin, people take a long time to become physically dependent on alcohol. In most cases physical dependence only results from several years of regular heavy drinking, without any dramatic symptoms giving an indication of what is happening. A person who is drug dependent may not realise it until for some reason drug use is halted. If dependence has developed, termination of use will result in *withdrawal symptoms*, the body's reaction to the removal of something it has grown to expect and has adjusted to. Most drinkers never drink long enough or in sufficient amounts to become physically dependent on alcohol. Even so, many do sometimes experience hangovers after an excessively convivial evening. These *may* be a mild form of physical withdrawal. Like many other drugs, alcohol, if used regularly, does lead to tolerance. People get used to its effects and are less influenced by a given amount than they were at first. It is often said that a man will 'learn to carry his ale'. Over years of heavy drinking this tolerance may lead to physical dependence that will only be discovered if the excessive drinker stops drinking.

While a great deal is known about the chemistry of ethyl alcohol, it is not usefully possible to make categorical statements about the effects of specific quantities. Alcohol affects people in different ways. Its effects depend upon a person's size, diet, rate of drinking, social setting, and mood. It is therefore not really very useful to indicate any 'safe' level of alcohol consumption. This too must depend upon the person and the occasion. It is not safe to drink much at a party if one intends to drive shortly afterwards. One may drink more if one does not have to travel.

Drinking

While alcoholism is, rightly, a major cause for concern, it must not be forgotten that most alcohol use is harmless and is certainly enjoyable and beneficial. People often need to take the edge off reality, to experience a changed state of consciousness, to feel mellow. Drinking alcohol is often a convenient and easy way to do this.

> 'Leez me on drink! it gies us mair
> Than either school or college;
> It kindles wit, it waukens lear,
> It pangs us fou o' knowledge:
> Be't whisky-gill or penny wheep,
> Or onie stronger potion,
> It never fails, on drinkin deep
> To kittle up our notion
> By night or day.'
> (Robert Burns)

Learning to drink

The great majority of adults in Britain drink alcohol at least occasionally (Edwards *et al.* 1972; Dight 1976; Plant and Pirie 1979). Alcohol is consequently part of the family environment of most people from a very early age. People learn about drinking in different ways and may completely change both their beliefs about alcohol and their drinking habits at different stages of their lives. Much of this book is concerned with examining such changes in people's *drinking careers*.

Two Glasgow, studies have examined what children of different ages know about alcohol, and how they start to drink (Jahoda and Cramond 1972; Davies and Stacey 1972).

Jahoda and Cramond found that even before primary school age most of the children in their study had encountered drunken adults. By the age of six the majority had experienced such encounters and could identify alcoholic drinks. Up to this point young children had neutral or mildly favourable attitudes to drinking. Between the ages of six to ten more became critical of drinking.

> 'An interpretation which fits the facts better is that children gradually learn that alcohol is frowned upon by people in such institutions as schools and church. It would not be surprising if, in an authority setting like the school, they responded in terms of their awareness of the prevailing disapproval.'
>
> (Jahoda and Cramond 1972: xiv)

The second Glasgow study examined drinking amongst young people aged fourteen to seventeen. This showed that as young people mature the influence of their homes diminishes and that of their teenage peer group becomes dominant. By the age of fourteen, 92 per cent of boys and 85 per cent of girls had tasted alcohol. Three years later only 2 per cent of boys and 4 per cent of girls were still totally abstinent. The negative attitudes of the pre-adolescent appear to change completely once a young person passes through puberty. Teenagers begin to define drinking and drinkers in their own terms. The drinker is viewed as sociable and tough, while the non-drinker is regarded as weak and unsociable, as rather an unattractive killjoy. Davies and Stacey found that, with increasing age, children consume more alcohol outside their homes. The influence of parents and 'officials' such as teachers is steadily replaced by that of their peers. Often teenagers will begin drinking in earnest furtively with friends in parks and streets. This is consistent with Canadian evidence that while *drinking* normally begins at home, youthful *drunkenness* usually occurs elsewhere (Smart 1976). Parents are very likely to be unaware of exactly how much their teenage children drink when with their peers (Cutler and Storm 1973). Young people begin drinking regularly because their friends do it and because their lifelong experience of alcohol consumption by adults has led them to accept drinking as a hallmark of maturity. There is little doubt that most young people begin drinking fairly often while they are still too young legally to purchase drinks in public bars. There is considerable social pressure amongst young people to drink. This is the generally accepted social ideal. Interestingly, while drinking in moderation appears generally approved, Davies and Stacey found that the heavy drinker is seen as tough, yet as *unsociable*; an individual who exceeds what is desired or allowed.

Most young people are brought up by parents who drink alcohol in moderation and who do not suffer any serious ill effects because of their drinking. A minority of children are not so lucky and have parents who misuse alcohol and who do suffer because of their drinking. Some children have parents who are teetotallers and who may strongly discourage others from drinking. Neither alcohol misusers nor abstainers are able to provide for their children a model of moderate drinking. Because this is the predominant social style of alcohol use this places children at a disadvantage when learning about alcohol. Many people who, later in life, get into trouble with their drinking come from families where such a model of moderate drinking was lacking. An investigation by Hawker (1978) collected self-administered questionnaire data from 7,278 school children aged thirteen to eighteen in five areas of England. This study indicated that the great majority of children had adopted their parents' pattern of drinking or abstinence. In addition, it appeared that parents who disapproved of drinking were more likely than parents who had a permissive approach to have children who were either abstainers or only occasional drinkers (Hawker 1978: 22). More than a quarter of the boys and slightly fewer girls considered the most important factor in encouraging young people to drink was 'being with adults you know well who drink regularly' (Hawker 1978: 15).

An interesting study of the influence of parental views on drinking and the subsequent behaviour of young people has been provided by O'Connor (1978). Comparison of English and Irish families indicated that English parents were rather casual and permissive in teaching their children about alcohol. In contrast, Irish parents were far more likely to discourage their children from drinking and this view was reinforced by the fact that most children took confirmation pledges not to drink at all until they were at least twenty-one. O'Connor found that, while some Irish children did remain non-drinkers, as a group they were in fact more likely than their English counterparts to get into difficulties through drinking. Ironically, some of those who did encounter problems did so even when consuming less alcohol than comparable English young people who were trouble-free. This study and the two Glasgow investigations are consistent with the view that most people begin to learn about drinking from their parents at home. Those who in later life appear most able to conform to the generally accepted norm of using alcohol (but in moderation) are those who began using it casually in a family setting. While it is clear that parental views may be accepted unquestioningly by younger children, teenagers are very likely, through contact with others of their own age, to begin drinking whatever their parents' attitudes are.

Social variations in drinking habits

Societies have widely differing views of alcohol. Not only do patterns of drinking vary enormously, but so do the types and importance of particular alcohol-related problems. One may distinguish four distinctly different types of cultural pattern in relation to drinking:

(1) *Abstinent culture*: Where the cultural attitude is hostile to and prohibitive of any type of alcohol consumption, e.g. Moslem and Hindu countries.

(2) *Ambivalent culture*: Where there is conflict over the use of alcohol between the 'wets' and 'drys', e.g. Scotland, France, or other countries where temperance movements oppose brewing and distilling interests.

(3) *Permissive culture*: Where drinking is freely permitted, but where drunkenness and harmful consequences are disdained, e.g. the Jews.

(4) There is also a fourth possibility, that of *over-permissive culture*. In such a situation not only drinking but drunkenness may be tolerated:

'In one sense this type, the *over-permissive culture*, does not occur completely in societies, but only approximations

in certain non-literate societies, in those cultures undergoing considerable social change, and those in which there
are strong economic vested interests in the production and
distribution of alcoholic beverages.'   (Pittman 1967: 5)

An interesting example of how the effects of alcohol vary
amongst different social groups is provided by a people called the
Camba. These are descended from Spanish colonists and
Amerindians living in Eastern Bolivia. They are relatively isolated,
having little contact with other groups of people. The Camba drink
a highly potent alcoholic beverage at their frequent festive occasions. They always drink socially, never alone. 'Both drinking and
drunkenness are the norm on these occasions and an integral part of
their social ritual. Drunkenness is consciously sought as an end in
itself, and consensus supports its value' (Heath 1962: 25-6). In spite
of these frequent binges, there is no evidence of alcohol dependence amongst the Camba, or even of hangovers. It is probably
important that solitary drinking is inconceivable to the Camba.
Drinking is regarded only as useful if it is a social act. It loses its
meaning unless one is in company. Heath (1962) suggests that this
very special, ritualized use of alcohol provides the Camba with their
major reference point and provides a sense of solidarity. Whatever
the explanation, the Camba illustrate that there is a lot more to
drinking and alcohol-related problems than just the effects of large
doses of a drug (alcohol) upon an individual.

It is not possible to make accurate statements about drinking
habits in different countries. As will be indicated in Chapter 3, data
in this field are simply not that precise, nor has a great amount of
research been done in most countries. Even so there is abundant
evidence that social groups do have their own widely differing ways
of drinking: the French, for example, imbibe, on average, far
greater quantities of alcohol than the British. Unlike the British,
they do not generally confine their drinking to one or two evening
sessions each week, but drink on most days, and often throughout
the day. In consequence, the French experience less acute drunkenness due to high consumption at one time than the British. The
French drinker is less likely to get blind drunk on a Friday, to crash
his car or to beat his wife, but more likely gradually to poison his
liver. Even within single countries there are big social differences in
the pattern of drinking habits. Scotland has traditionally had far

greater levels of alcohol-related problems than England and Wales (Grant 1976). A study of drinking habits in four Scottish towns revealed not only that each town had its own characteristic percentage of abstainers, light, and heavy drinkers: each town also had quite different rates of alcohol-related problems. The level of problems was broadly consistent with the average level of alcohol consumption (i.e. a high consumption town had a high level of problems). Even so, it was evident that the small differences in consumption levels could hardly be expected to explain the fact that Inverness, for example, had far higher rates of alcohol-related problems than Ayr (Plant and Pirie 1979). Local traditions and attitudes to drinking, as O'Connor has shown, do exert a strong influence on how people behave when they are drinking. This point has been made succinctly by Makela (1977):

'To take a somewhat extreme example, we have no reason to believe that the French would start drunken fights should they lower their alcohol consumption to the same level as the Scots or Finns. Conversely, it remains to be seen whether the Finns or Scots stop fighting just because their average consumption is increasing.'

A major study of American drinking habits indicated the importance of local attitudes in determining the level of alcohol-related problems (Cahalan and Room 1974). This investigation showed that the highest rates of alcohol-related problems were in the 'wet' areas where most adults drank alcohol and there were relatively few abstainers. Interestingly, the areas with intermediate levels of problems were not areas of intermediate alcohol use, but were the 'dry' areas, where there were the fewest drinkers and the most abstainers. In such areas drinking was generally disapproved of, and people were unlikely to drink for purely casual, social reasons. In such areas, drinking is made into a deviant activity, and is both attractive to unusual or deviant people and becomes a furtive, guilt-ridden form of behaviour, much as heroin use is in Britain today. It is an interesting speculation that the rural Scottish Highlands and Islands may have a much higher alcoholism rate than the rest of Britain because of the strength there of religious views which are hostile to drinking.

Alcohol is an important part of social life. From a very early age most people are bombarded with impressions about it which are reinforced by expensive and sophisticated advertising. Alcohol is a useful 'social glue', relieving tensions, facilitating social contacts, and symbolizing friendship. While moderate drinking is harmless, excessive or unwise use can lead to a constellation of difficulties which are summarized in the following section.

Drinking problems: definition

'Alcohol is a potentially addictive drug and if misused a substance that gives pleasure can lead to insidious but finally incapacitating illness. The reasons for alcohol being misused lie not only in the individual but in his society: if the environment is permissive toward excessive drinking, then excessive drinking will go unchecked.'   (Edwards 1975: 1297)

Many definitions of 'alcoholism' have been suggested. The best-known is certainly that put forward in 1951 by the World Health Organization:

'Alcoholics are those excessive drinkers whose dependence on alcohol has attained such a degree that they show a noticeable mental disturbance or an interference with their mental and bodily health, their interpersonal relations and their smooth social and economic functioning; or who show the prodromal signs of such developments. They therefore require treatment.'

Most definitions of alcoholism contain three elements:

(1) physical dependence or 'addiction'
(2) physical damage
(3) social problems.

There are a 'syndrome' or group of alcohol-related problems or disabilities (Edwards *et al.* 1977). People may experience none, one, several, or many of these problems, so that it is, in fact, debatable at what precise point a person should properly be referred to as an 'alcoholic'. In fact, people contacting alcoholism treatment agencies are a very mixed group. A minority have serious physical damage. Some, though not all, will be physically dependent upon alcohol and most will probably have experienced some form of social problems in connection with their drinking. All they have in common is some type of (usually long-term) problem somehow associated with their misuse of alcohol.

The popular (mis)conception of the alcoholic is that of a social derelict, typically a middle-aged or elderly male on Skid Row and imbibing unlikely beverages such as metal polish or meths. In fact, only a small percentage of known alcoholics are social derelicts. Most are still in employment and, as Chapter 2 describes, many have very high-status jobs. Most alcoholics are, in fact, unremarkable people who drink the same mundane beverages (cider, lager, beer, wine, spirits) as the rest of the community. A growing proportion of those getting into trouble with their drinking are females and a growing proportion are young.

People who get into difficulties with their drinking do not conform to any narrow stereotype. They are a very varied group, as are the problems they encounter.

Physical dependence or 'addiction'. The process of tolerance leading to physical dependence has been described earlier in this chapter in relation to the properties of alcohol as a drug. Physical dependence upon alcohol usually takes several years to develop, and typically this happens gradually and unnoticed as a person gets used to drinking heavily and regularly. As tolerance to alcohol develops, a person needs to drink more to gain the original effects. Later, if liver damage is caused, this process will be reversed as the body's ability to oxidize alcohol is impaired. At this stage, the drinker will find that the effects of a given amount of alcohol increase. Withdrawal symptoms signify that a person is physically dependent upon alcohol. They occur either when a person stops drinking altogether or greatly reduces his level of alcohol consumption. Withdrawal symptoms similar to those of barbiturate withdrawal may occur within a few hours, or may take several days to appear. The most common early sign of withdrawal is acute tremulousness, better known as 'the shakes'. Typically a dependent drinker will experience the shakes in the morning following the fall in blood alcohol level during sleep.

'The principal feature is gross shaking of the hands, made worse if he tries to do anything with them. Sometimes he complains of a feeling of weakness. Agitation and tremor can reach such a degree that he may not be able to sit still, to dress himself or to pour out a drink without spilling it. Usually the condition disappears fairly rapidly as more drink is taken but without alcohol it may persist for as long as a week or more.'

(Kessel and Walton 1974: 34)

Withdrawal may be accompanied by hallucinations. In milder cases they may be brief. If the person has been drinking excessively for many years, withdrawal symptoms are likely to be more severe. At their most dramatic, hallucinations may reach the scale of delirium tremens (DTs). This condition is one of the severest, if not the severest, types of drug withdrawal symptom. Delirium tremens may not occur for several days after the cessation of, or great reduction in, drinking. Typically, the sufferer experiences extreme fear often accompanied by nightmarish hallucinations, often of small animals such as bats, rats, and mice (*not* pink elephants, as often maintained). In many ways delirium tremens resembles a bad LSD trip. The effects of LSD usually wear off in six or seven hours. Delirium tremens may persist for two to three days, usually culminating in deep sleep. Sometimes, if untreated, people may die from alcohol withdrawal as from withdrawal from other drugs. This is usually caused by depression of respiration. Fits or alcoholic epilepsy may occur, but are not common in Britain. Fortunately, medical care, using drugs, can greatly relieve the unpleasantness of withdrawal from alcohol. Recovery, which is termed 'drying out' can generally be achieved in a week or ten days at most.

Physical damage. Excessive drinking can cause a wide range of physical disabilities. The most widespread and serious of these involve the liver. Reversible fatty liver and hepatitis and irreversible liver cirrhosis are frequent consequences of excessive drinking. With liver cirrhosis, healthy liver tissues become replaced by scar tissues. If drinking is discontinued, the liver does not usually get worse, but cannot recover. Liver cirrhosis, if not arrested, is a fatal condition. At least 70 per cent of those who die from liver cirrhosis in Britain are known to be excessive drinkers. There is evidence indicating that females are more vulnerable than males to acute liver disease (Krasner 1978).

Gastritis (inflamed stomach) and peptic ulcers are also common alcohol-related disabilities. These are reversible only in their early stages. Alcoholics are commonly deficient in vitamin B. One result is impaired memory. Selective amnesias or blackouts of recent events, even though recollection of earlier events is undamaged, may occur. These are often manifested by people being unable to remember incidents from the previous day, for example, how they drove home. These are not to be confused with states of drunkenness leading to insensibility. These amnesias are known as *Korsakov's Syndrome*, named after a Russian psychiatrist who described them. This condition is usually irreversible.

'It is almost unbelievable how short-lived the patient's memory can be. One patient awoke each morning believing he had been admitted to hospital during the previous night. Another, after weeks in the ward, still required to read the names at the foot of each bed in order to find his own when returning from the lavatory. Yet so well were his other faculties preserved that, failing to remember investments, he had lost a fortune as a stockbroker over the past few months without anyone realizing he was ill. To compensate for the memory loss the patient confabulates; he invents circumstances to fill the gaps and cover up.'

(Kessel and Walton 1974: 38)

The memory is likely to remain damaged. A reversible confusional state, *Wernicke's Syndrome*, sometimes occurs. This sometimes also involves amnesias, paralysis of the eyeball, and difficulty in moving. It is also caused by vitamin B deficiency. Continued excessive drinking may cause a number of other mental and physical disabilities. These may include gradual diminution of intellectual capacity, anaemia, acute and chronic pancreatitis, haemorrhoids, loss of sensation in nerve fibres, muscle pains, and, in men, irreversible atrophy of the testes. In addition, excessive drinking greatly increases the risk of heart disease, tuberculosis, emphysema, and cancer of the pharynx (Kessel and Walton 1974: 37-42; Einstein 1975: 78-9). Not the least of the physical consequences of excessive drinking is sexual impotence, colloquially referred to, in males, as 'brewers' droop'.

Social problems.   Most people who begin to worry about their drinking habits probably do so because of social problems rather than because they discover they are dependent or have suffered severe physical damage. In most cases an individual will not concede that his or her drinking is out of hand until a major tragedy of some sort occurs. The list is almost endless. At work absenteeism and accidents are commonplace (Hore 1977; Schramm 1977). In consequence, dismissal from work is often the crisis that forces an individual to acknowledge the excessiveness of his drinking. Domestic strife is also a frequent consequence. The excessive drinker may well get himself and his family into debt (a bottle of whisky daily could cost at least £30 to £35 each week). Many of the social problems associated with alcohol are problems of *drunkenness* rather than problems of alcohol dependence. The latter usually takes several years to develop, whereas a person may get into grave difficulties because of a single instance of heavy drinking. The distinction between 'alcoholism' (involving physical dependence on alcohol) and drunkenness is an important one. Many alcoholics report that they never get drunk and most people who do get drunk are certainly not alcoholics. The toll of Friday and Saturday night drinking is all too well known. Traffic accidents, often fatal, outbreaks of violence on the streets, in public houses, wife (or husband) beating, baby battering, murder — there is no doubt that the misuse of alcohol has an important part to play in such tragic events. A great deal of these behaviours involve people socially, often influenced in their actions by belief that drinking is associated with toughness and masculinity (*N.B.* Davies and Stacey 1972). Drunkenness is so common largely owing to the commonplace habit of confining drinking to relatively restricted sessions. If a man who drinks twenty-one pints a week spreads his consumption evenly, at three pints a day, he will be unlikely to get into trouble through drinking. If, on the other hand, he drinks his 'ration' during two short sessions, he will almost certainly get drunk and may get into all manner of difficulties because of this.

Excessive drinking may, therefore, lead to acute difficulties without necessarily causing dependence. Once a person has become dependent, drinking will often be maintained to ward off unpleasant withdrawal symptoms. At this stage, 'relief drinking' may be engaged in upon wakening to get rid of the shakes. Alcoholism, and its attendant problems, such as dismissal from employment, road accidents, and marital discord, is also associated with very high suicide rates (Stengel 1964) and alcohol is often used when people take overdoses (Kreitman 1977).

Social and cultural factors

It has already been indicated earlier in this chapter how greatly drinking habits vary from one social group to the next. Family background, religion, and nationality are major determinants of drinking behaviour in general, and of the risks a person runs of encountering alcohol-related problems. *In general, the traditional way a social group uses alcohol influences alcohol-related problems, and probably does so regardless of genetic or personality factors, though these too may play a part.* There is extensive evidence that both drinking habits and alcohol-related problems vary greatly even within a single country. People of different ages and of different social classes have different drinking habits: males differ in their drinking habits from females. Different occupational groups also appear to have very varied drinking habits and rates of alcohol-related problems. This is the primary concern of this book and the evidence to support this belief is reviewed in Chapter 2.

2 Alcoholism and occupation

Some occupations have long been associated with drunkenness and alcoholism. Expressions such as 'drunk as a judge' or 'drunk as a cooper' are commonplace. The drunken doctor is almost a compulsory figure in any good Western film. There is a great deal of evidence that much of this folk lore is correct. Some occupations do have especially high rates of alcoholism and it is possible to draw some general conclusions about why this is so. In this chapter some of the extensive evidence relating alcoholism to specific occupations is described and likely explanations are suggested.

We know that some occupations have high rates of alcoholism largely because of three types of information: first, there are detailed studies of specific occupational groups which have revealed particularly high rates of alcohol-related problems. Second, there is information from alcoholism treatment agencies showing that people in certain occupations are disproportionately likely to come forward for help. Third, there are national liver cirrhosis mortality data showing that some occupations have particularly high rates of death due to liver disease which is mainly related to excessive drinking. In addition, there is some information from population surveys of differing drinking habits amongst different social class groups. While not strictly occupational categories, these do help to complete the general impression of how non-manual workers are likely to differ in their alcohol use or misuse from manual workers.

Occupational studies

Seamen. The association between seafaring and heavy drinking has long posed the question, 'What shall we do with the drunken sailor?'. An interesting commentary on this occupational hazard is provided by a writer who himself was a sailor and who became an abstinent alcoholic.

> 'Ashore, part of the heritage of the sea are the visits to the houses of prostitution and the saloons or places where drink flows freely ... new men are introduced to strange local drinks — cooliehow, saki, calvados or any other local wines, rums or whiskies. Then follows introductions to girls who would not receive a second glance from the same men sober ... Their first objective is to outdo the old timers in regards to both women and liquor, until they have built up a tolerance and accustomed themselves to this life.' (J.I.F. 1947)

The same writer explains that on board ship men have few emotional outlets and use their periods ashore to relieve their pent-up tensions, often with the aid of alcohol.

Several studies have indicated that alcoholism is especially prevalent amongst seamen. Powdermaker (1945) and Heath (1945) found that, of a group of American merchant seamen passing through merchant marine rest centres, about a fifth were alcoholic. A study of ninety-four hospitalized alcoholics who were in the United States Navy and Marines led to the conclusion that those men had become alcoholic largely due to encouragement to participate in heavy drinking in their work situations (Wallinga 1956). Similar conclusions were reached from an interview study of 100 British merchant seamen (Rose and Glatt 1961). The authors commented that amongst merchant seamen there is an especially great risk of alcoholism, partly due to the occupational acceptance or encouragement of heavy drinking. In addition, they speculated that the Merchant Navy may attract men with personalities particularly prone to develop alcoholism. This view was suggested by the fact that many of their subjects exhibited such traits. A major limitation of this suggestion is that personality traits already evident amongst the study group of merchant seamen may have been consequences of, rather than causes of, heavy drinking or alcoholism.

Brun-Gulbrandsen and Irgens-Jensen (1967) examined a representative sample of 3,447 young Norwegian naval conscripts. They identified 14 per cent of these as serious misusers of alcohol. The authors concluded that alcohol was a major problem amongst sailors. They echoed Rose and Glatt's assertion that this is at least partly due to the recruitment of people predisposed to misuse alcohol. Another Norwegian study by Arner (1973) reviewed the high accident rates amongst seamen. This study indicated that at least a third of fatalities were connected with excessive drinking. Arner also concluded that perhaps seafaring attracts particular types of men, specifically those who are accident-prone.

Schuckit and Gunderson (1974) examined the job types of 1,701 United States Navy enlisted men who were hospitalized for alcoholism. This investigation suggested that the occupational preferences of naval alcoholics resembled those of civilian alcoholics, which are described later in this chapter. 'The concentration of alcoholics in jobs of service and commerce and semi-skilled labour have their counterparts in the Navy's Administrative-Clerical, Deck and Construction groups, while technical jobs have low alcoholism rates in both populations' (Schuckit and Gunderson 1974: 583).

Schuckit and Gunderson did not find evidence to support the view that alcoholism was related to job dissatisfaction. Like some of the researchers mentioned above, they suggested that the link between alcoholism and types of job might have been due to selection factors rather than the effects of being in a specific job situation. For example, 'high-risk' jobs tended to be non-technical, with a high proportion of older men and a high proportion from working-class backgrounds. If this is so, age and social class may have been the explanation rather than occupation.

'Consumption of Alcohol has been associated with the sailor's way of life for centuries. From medieval to modern times the British Navy regularly issued rations of rum, beer, or wine to men at sea, depending on local circumstances. For example, "in the Mediterranean, where beer would not keep, each man was allowed in lieu of one gallon of beer, one pint of sound, strong wine for each day" (Keevil 1958). The first note on drinking problems by a US Navy medical officer was by Dr H.G. Beyer in the Navy's *Medical Bulletin* in April 1908 long before Josephus Daniels banished grog from US ships during Woodrow Wilson's administration. The first report in the public literature on psychosis in the Navy called attention to the fact that the Government Hospital for the Insane in Washington, DC had 69 Navy and Marine Corps patients, most of whom had conditions resulting from alcohol consumption or syphilis (Butts 1910).'

(Kolb and Gunderson 1977: 183)

More recently naval alcoholism has been a major source of concern. The situation in the United States Navy has been extensively researched and is well described by Kolb and Gunderson (1977). These investigators refer to the social expectations within the Navy that men (and women) will drink, and to the fact that cheap alcoholic drinks are available to all ranks.

'Estimates of prevalence in the naval population vary from 7% "addicted" alcoholics (the same rate as in the civilian work force) to 38% "problem drinkers" in the Cahalan and Cisin study; estimates of financial losses caused by alcoholism in the Navy range from $188 million to $475 million. Such figures are based on self-report, surveys, general impressions or tentative opinions rather than on hard data.'   (Kolb and Gunderson 1977: 184)

There is no doubt that alcoholism in the United States Navy is a big problem, which has led to the establishment of specialized treatment facilities aptly dubbed 'drydocks'. Kolb and Gunderson report that series of investigations have been carried out on naval conscripts hospitalized between 1965 and 1971 and for men treated in alcoholism rehabilitation centres and units from 1972 to mid-1974. This research shows that the typical male Marine Corps alcoholic was thirty-three years old upon first admission and had served for thirteen years:

'Overall alcoholism incidence rates for Navy and Marine Corps conscripts were 74 and 44 respectively. For both groups there was a sharp increase in incidence rate with age: for the Navy the rate for men over the age of 40 was 410 per 100,000; for the Marine Corps, the rate was approximately 330 per 100,000. Male Navy and Marine Corps officers were eight to nine years older than their enlisted counterparts at the time of first hospital admission for alcoholism. The mean number of years of service for the combined officer groups was 19.4 years ... The incidence rate for

Navy officers increased sharply with ranks — from 25 per 100,000 for lieutenants to 81 per 100,000 for captains and above ... The incidence rate for Navy and Marine Corps enlisted women was 90 per 100,000 — the highest rate for any group studied.'   (Kolb and Gunderson 1977: 181)

Investigation of the job types which had the highest alcoholism rates showed that high-risk jobs were mainly non-technical, while low-risk jobs were mainly skilled or technical. There was an association between high-risk jobs and high socio-economic status (Kolb and Gunderson 1977: 191).

The problem of alcoholism in the British fishing industry has been thoroughly and interestingly reviewed by Rix, Hunter, and Olley (1977). From this review, it is clear that the fishing industry has long suffered a tragic toll of accidents and even major disasters probably or possibly due to misusing alcohol. The Holland-Martin Report on trawler safety (Board of Trade 1969) stated that some men set sail under the influence of alcohol who were obviously unfit to work efficiently. The Report stated that alcohol was a likely reason for many trawler accidents.

A more recent inquiry by the Department of Trade (1975) concluded with apparent relief that not more than 15 per cent of fishermen were immoderate drinkers, and disputed that this percentage was higher than amongst the general population. In fact, as Rix, Hunter, and Olley point out, the accidental death rate of Scottish fishermen is seven times higher than for the general population, so this optimism may be ill-founded. In order to illuminate this issue, Rix, Hunter, and Olley examined the incidence of hospitalization for alcoholism of fishermen in the north-east of Scotland. Using the local computer-based psychiatric case register they ascertained the numbers of men who had received a first diagnosis of alcoholism. Relating these records to the occupational structure of the area's total population, fishermen proved to be between one-and-a-half and four times as likely as the rest of the working male population to be treated for alcoholism. The authors found that, in most cases of diagnosed alcoholism amongst the fishermen in their study, there appeared to be clear reasons for that problem. Some fishermen reported having strongly teetotal parents or parents who were alcoholics. Others had become heavy drinkers while in the armed forces or other 'high-risk' jobs, such as being barmen or salesmen. This study led the authors to contradict the frequently expressed view that alcoholism is not a problem in the fishing industry. They concluded, in the words of Sir Walter Scott in *The Antiquary*: 'It's no fish ye'r buying, it's men's lives'.

Lawyers. The heavy drinking of the legal profession has been often referred to in anecdote. Rix (1978) in an account of the alcoholism of James Boswell notes that Boswell wrote that he 'saw tonight what I never saw before: a company of advocates free from drunkenness' (Scott and Pottle 1933). Boswell also gave an interesting description of the drinking of one of his colleagues:

> I found the solicitor, who had been with us last night and drank very heavily, standing in the outer Hall (of the Parliament House) looking very ill. He had struggled to attend his business, but it would not do. Peter Murray told me he had seen him this morning come out of a Dram Shop in the Back Stairs, in all his formalities of large wig and cravat. He had been trying to settle his stomach.'

Domestic servants.   While social changes have greatly reduced the numbers of people working 'below stairs', there is evidence that domestic servants have a high rate of excessive drinking. Straus and Winterbottom (1949) interviewed ninety-nine female domestic servants in an American town. In addition they interviewed 117 women employing such servants. This investigation included seventy-seven matched employer-employee pairs. The results showed that the level of alcohol use, especially frequent spirit drinking, was higher amongst domestic servants than amongst the general local population. In spite of this there was no evidence of excessive drinking leading to problems. The investigators suggest that perhaps women working in such situations will rapidly be detected if they do develop problems and are likely to be dismissed. This theory may apply to others in relatively low-status occupations, where the problem drinker, if noticed as such, might be much more likely to be dismissed than higher-status workers.

Straus and Winterbottom noted that important features of the job situations of female domestic servants were their close supervision and lack of privacy. In consequence their social and, particularly, their sexual behaviour were unusually restricted. These constraints may well have explained the apparent frequency of heavy drinking.

Company directors. Roman and Trice (1972) studied in detail three large American companies in which senior executives were known to be alcoholics. They concluded that if a senior figure is alcoholic, his subordinates use his incapacity to assume more power and responsibility for themselves. In this way the alcoholic's disadvantages are exploited and even fostered. While this study does not explain the causes of alcoholism amongst company directors or senior executives, it indicates that sometimes alcoholism may be tolerated rather than regarded as cause for concern.

Military personnel. The high rates of excessive drinking amongst both civilian and military seamen have already been indicated. There is an extensive literature showing that the armed forces in general have a high risk of alcohol-related problems (e.g. Maletsky and Klotter 1975; Sclare 1978).

Barrett (1943) reported that, between 1937 and 1942, 16 per cent of males admitted to the Veteran's Hospital at Knoxville in Iowa were diagnosed as alcoholics. Reviewing the case histories of 100 such alcoholic ex-servicemen he suggested that their alcoholism was possibly attributable to their former work situations. Harrington and Price (1962) concluded that American ex-servicemen who were alcoholics had become heavy drinkers during their military service. Carney (1963), examining British servicemen stationed in Cyprus, reported that they were subject to strong pressures to drink heavily while in military messes. The special pressures of military life are well described by Gwinner (1976), who suggests that service life is characterized by five features. First, it is hierarchical, uniformed, and demands conformity: there is strong pressure to be 'one of the boys'. Military life produces boredom and generates frustrations. Alcohol offers a means of escaping from inhibitions and from the constraints of service life. Second, alcoholic servicemen are protected from the consequences of their excessive drinking by the paternalism of military life. 'The serviceman is protected from reaching rock bottom ... Paternalism can provide a luxuriant medium for the development of the alcoholic condition' (Gwinner 1976: 25). The third feature is that the military milieu is tolerant of alcohol use. The suggestion here is that because servicemen in general are highly likely to be drinkers, some are likely to become alcoholic. Fourth, like those in the Merchant Navy and certain other 'high-risk' occupations, servicemen have to move more frequently and in consequence have a less stable home life. The fifth factor is the relative absence of women from military life: 'The absence of women in the work force appears to remove a significant control and to encourage "Let's all be boys together" attitudes which promote excessive drinking' (Gwinner 1976: 25). A similar comment has been made in relation to the United States' forces:

'Since the military as a social organism tends, by virtue of its paradoxical emphasis on masculinity and lack of autonomy simultaneously, to encourage the "romance of alcohol" in which alcohol is seen to increase courage, sexual attractiveness and power, skilfulness and happiness, a powerful source of counter-propaganda is necessary to reduce alcohol abuse.'

(Long, Hewitt, and Blane 1977: 116)

The medical profession. It is an old adage that to be an alcoholic one has to drink more than one's doctor does. Sometimes, sadly, this is no mean feat since there is abundant evidence that doctors themselves have a very high alcoholism rate.

'Alcoholism is not a subject particularly well understood by the medical profession. With every specialist understandably pressing for his own particular interest to be given added attention in the undergraduate curriculum, alcoholism is generally lucky if it is accorded so much as a lecture or two. Small wonder then that the doctor who is beginning to drink too much does not understand what is happening to him, and his colleagues often do not know how to respond helpfully.

For the doctor alcoholic, the familiar history is therefore of a period of very dangerous drinking during which his colleagues have turned a blind eye, with the story then developing to a crisis which is met with misunderstanding and rejection. This biphasic course is predictable.

Illustrations of connivance are many. A surgeon has obviously unsteady hands, but no-one likes to do anything positive. He is persuaded on bad days to let his registrar take the list. A consultant physician is drunk on teaching rounds and is simply regarded as a well-known figure of fun. The anaesthetist is too hung-over to function properly, but somehow keeps going on a handful of swallowed chlordiazepoxide. A general practitioner is propped up by his partners, though well-known in the locality for his habits. When everything else fails, the doctor whose reputation is otherwise such as to make him unemployable can keep going as a perpetual locum, with no questions asked. A houseman presents problems, but the reference is duly written which helps him to his next job.'   (Edwards 1975: 1297)

Not surprisingly, there are many general references to this problem in the medical literature (e.g. Ludlam 1976, Noie 1977).

'The prime occupational hazard in the practice of medicine is the disease of addiction to alcohol and to other drugs.

The hazard, currently widespread among our whole population, is exceptionally great for the physician for a number of reasons: many times the doctor finds it necessary to prescribe drugs to patients who have exactly the same symptoms which he himself experiences; the "invincibility ethos" so carefully developed in medical school makes it difficult for the physician to admit a personal problem; the stress of professional responsibility and obligation is ever present, ever increasing, while time for relaxation becomes an increasingly rare commodity; and a wide variety of mood-changing drugs is always instantly available, with no questions asked. It becomes very tempting, very easy, to turn to a mood-changing drug — alcohol or whatever — when time is short and pressures are many.'

            (Talbott, Shoemaker, Follo, and Bullard 1976: 77)

As the preceding quotation shows, the most commonly suggested explanation for the high rate of alcoholism amongst doctors is availability of addictive substances combined with public expectations that doctors are superhuman. 'The pressures of medical practice, as well as the ready availability of drugs and alcohol, put physicians into a high risk category for these problems' (Ludlam 1976: 10).

Murray (1976) compared the alcoholism rates in Scotland of hospitalized male doctors with those of other male patients of comparable social status. This investigation showed that the rate amongst doctors was more than two-and-a-half times higher than amongst other professional men. 'Middle-aged doctors were particularly at risk, and 58% of all psychiatric hospitalizations of male doctors between the ages of 45 and 54 years were attributed to alcoholism' (Murray 1976: 729-30).

This study is a valuable one since much of the discussion of the supposedly high alcoholism rate amongst doctors has not been based upon properly controlled investigations. Some studies referred to highly atypical hospitals or clinics which, since they were high prestige institutes, might be especially likely to attract doctors (e.g. A. Brook *et al*. 1967; Franklin 1977).

Murray comments that: 'The special position of doctors in relation to medical treatment and factors such as their greater access to psychiatrists may have contributed to their higher rates, but it is improbable that they accounted for much of this excess' (1976:730).

Murray qualifies his findings by noting that the exceptionally high alcoholism rate amongst his subjects is probably influenced by the fact that they were all males and were Scottish. He suggests that one influential factor explaining the high alcoholism rate amongst doctors is their relatively high income, and ability to afford to buy alcohol.

While there is considerable evidence that qualified doctors have a particularly high alcoholism rate, less is known about when they begin to be 'at risk'. In addition to the peculiar professional stresses already mentioned, it has been suggested that heavy or excessive drinking may begin at medical school (Duffy and Litin 1964). It has certainly been shown that some medical students do undergo severe stresses while in training and that alcohol abuse is one possible consequence (Thomas 1976).

The problems of suicide and drug abuse amongst American doctors has been reviewed by Bressler (1976). This review indicated that 40 per cent of doctor suicides were associated with alcoholism, and that the incidence of alcoholism not leading to suicide is also high amongst physicians. Bressler suggests several factors that place the medical profession at particular risk in relation to suicide, alcoholism, or other forms of drug dependence. These include role strain, demanding patients, overwork, fatigue, and long hours. Bressler suggests that some doctors attempt to deny their dependency needs by turning to overwork. In addition, some 'succumb to the temptation to be authority figures rather than human beings' (Bressler 1976: 173).

Newly qualified doctors are subject to greater professional strains since the identity formed in training is, for the first time, really put to the test: 'He finds himself in a difficult position, feeling that he does not like the practice of medicine. This explains why the onset of addiction and the peak suicide rate occur after the physician has been practising only a few years' (Bressler 1976: 175).

Perhaps the greatest single reason for the high alcoholism rate amongst doctors is the failure of current medical training to make students as aware of their own problems as they should be of those of their patients. Recurring constantly through discussions of physician alcoholism is the theme that the doctor is programmed to conform to a role which does not concede the possibility of personal distress or illness.

Alcohol production workers. The drink trade have long been popularly associated with problems of alcohol abuse. An interesting insight into the drinking habits of brewery workers in comparison with other occupations is provided by an Austrian study:

> 'Experience has shown that this group of workers has an abnormally high beer consumption, due to the fact that each worker receives a substantial daily allowance of beer, plus the fact that consumption of beer at work is frequently uncontrolled. Heavy drinking for the brewery worker therefore carries no financial burden, consequently he has the opportunity to imbibe limitless quantities of beer.'   (Frank, Heil, and Leadolter 1967: 892-93)

The Austrian researchers collected self-reported alcohol consumption data and medical histories from 200 male brewers aged twenty to sixty-five, together with two comparison groups. These were 100 metal workers in an engineering firm close to the brewery and 150 workers from a metallurgical firm further away. This investigation showed that liver damage had occurred in 34 per cent of the brewers, a far higher rate than in either of the two comparison groups. This difference was associated with the fact that the brewers were far heavier drinkers than the other two groups examined. The proportion of heavy drinkers amongst the brewers was twice as high as that amongst the other workers. The researchers noticed that most of those suffering liver damage were more or less free from side effects, and apparently fit for work. They suggested that drink trade workers need to be made aware of the damage of excessive drinking to the liver. They attributed the high rate of liver damage amongst the brewers to the availability of alcohol. One interesting conclusion was that the metal workers employed near the brewery appeared to have adopted the heavy drinking habits of their neighbours the brewers.

Alcoholics known to treatment agencies.   Most alcoholics do not come forward to be counted. It is known that general practitioners and other professionals probably identify only a minority of the alcoholics they do encounter (Wilkins 1974). It is clearly possible, if not probable, that alcoholics known to treatment agencies may differ from those who remain unrecorded. It cannot, therefore, be assumed that 'known' alcoholics typify those in the general population. There have been many descriptions of alcoholics in clinic populations. A few of these are summarized to indicate what types of conclusions these present.

Clark (1949) reviewed the incomes and occupational prestige of 1,695 white male alcoholics admitted to Chicago hospitals between 1922 and 1934. This review indicated that alcoholic psychosis admission rates were negatively correlated with income and occupational prestige. Clark concluded that alcoholism was most widespread amongst the lower-status individuals in his study group.

Amark (1970), reviewing 199 Swedish hospitalized alcoholics, found that commercial travellers, seamen, and those in literary and artistic occupations were over-represented. Commercial travellers were thirteen times as frequent amongst his group of alcoholics as they were in the general adult population. Amark commented that iron-plate workers, coppersmiths, butchers, dyers, drycleaners, and shoemakers were also over-represented.

'Lemere, Maxwell and O'Hollaren (1956) reviewed 7,828 private patients treated for alcoholism in Washington 1935-1955. They found that 20.0% of the study group were businessmen or executives, 5.0% were professionals and 8.0% were housewives. The "average patient" was described as: "male labourer, businessman or executive of approximately 40 years of age". This study revealed a higher proportion of businessmen and executives than were in the overall population of Washington. This very high proportion was certainly influenced by the fact that this review related only to private patients, who would be especially likely to be from high status occupational groups better able to afford private treatment.

Carney and Lawes (1967) compared 20 British male alcoholic patients with non-alcoholic patients and a control group. They concluded that it was not possible from their study to establish any relationship between occupation and alcoholism. Even so they stated that alcoholic patients were more likely than others to have attained senior rank during military service. The number of patients reviewed was too small to permit generalizing, since there are no grounds for assuming that the study group was representative.

Glatt (1967) noted that of 50 British private patients he had treated during two years, 24 were company directors and 10 were managers or senior executives. Private patients are certainly not representative of the general hospital population. As Spratley (1969) suggests, high status groups, such as company directors, may escape inclusion in many studies due to their frequent recourse to private medical facilities which are less likely to be surveyed.

Mayer and Myerson (1970) examined the characteristics of 393 out-patients at a Boston alcoholism clinic. They found that social status was not related to drinking history, or childhood family situation, but was related to police arrest experience and unemployment. These findings do not lend support to the view that some occupations have especially high alcoholism rates.

Spratley (1969) sent self-administered questionnaires to 700 male Alcoholics Anonymous members and private alcoholic patients. Preliminary results showed no clear evidence that occupation bore a causal relationship to alcoholism. Spratley concluded, ''... this preliminary investigation has indicated which occupations are potentially the most fruitful, namely the company director group. It has also been indicated that the regular services group is unlikely to be worth pursuing.'

(Plant 1977: 310)

Wilkins (1974), in a questionnaire survey of 546 patients attending a Manchester health centre, found that alcoholics were significantly more likely than other patients to be in the lower social classes.

Hore and Smith (1973) reviewed the biographical characteristics of 334 alcoholic patients in fifteen treatment units in England and Wales. The patients in this study group were from all occupational levels, but some occupations were over-represented in relation to the overall community: seamen, public house, hotel, and restaurant workers, publicans and hoteliers, nurses, medical practitioners, and company directors. Hore and Smith found that a higher proportion of the patients in their review were from social class 1 than were the overall patient population of England and Wales. This study is especially useful since several geographically separate clinics and hospitals were included.

In 1973, Merseyside Council on Alcoholism conducted a survey of the occupations of 2,000 alcoholics in the Liverpool area. Seventy-five per cent of these were still in employment:

> 'It was discovered that there were some three hundred and sixty-four individual professions or occupations with a fairly even distribution over the five social classes — perhaps with a preponderance in social classes 1, 2 and 3. It was found that the highest number were housewives without a full-time job.'

These findings did not indicate any clear relationship between alcoholism and occupation. The preponderance of people from social classes 1, 2, and 3 may be due to the fact that these groups are more likely to seek help of an agency such as AA, rather than an accurate reflection of the incidence of alcoholism in the general population.

Such studies of alcoholics known to treatment agencies are inconclusive. Some (Amark 1970; Clark 1949; Glatt 1967; Hore and Smith 1973; Lemere *et al.* 1956; Spratley 1969; Wilkins 1972) indicate that some occupations do have especially high alcoholism rates, while others (Carney and Lawes 1967; Mayer and Myerson 1970) do not. Most treatment institutions probably have contact with atypical subgroups of all the alcoholics in the community. No single institution is likely to be a fair reflection of the overall prevalence of alcoholism and therefore one cannot generalize safely from these groups of patients.

Mortality rates

Liver cirrhosis.   As noted in Chapter 1, it is generally accepted that one of the best indicators of the extent of alcoholism is the rate of death due to liver cirrhosis. The Registrar General's Office and the Office of Population Censuses and Surveys have produced occupational mortality statistics which throw interesting light upon the differing occupational risks of alcoholism. *Table 1* shows the twenty-four occupational groups (for males) in England and Wales which had the highest liver cirrhosis standardized mortality ratios*

---

* Standardized mortality ratios are calculated taking into account the age composition of an occupational group. The average ratio is 100.

(SMRs) in 1961. Each of these groups had at least twice the average rate of mortality from this cause.

Table 1 High-risk groups: male liver cirrhosis mortality (England and Wales 1961)

Occupational group	Standardized mortality ratio
Publicans and innkeepers	773
Stage managers, actors, entertainers, musicians	550
Deck engineering officers and ships' pilots	467
Cooks	460
Lodging house, hotel keepers, housekeepers and stewards	450
Deck and engine ratings, barge and boatmen	400
Armed forces (Commonwealth and overseas)	400
Armed forces (UK)	350
Medical practitioners	350
Finance, insurance brokers, financial agents	333
Textile, fabric, and related products makers and examiners	300
Electrical engineers	300
Restauranteurs, waiters, canteen hands	282
Service, sport, and recreation workers	241
Garage proprietors	233
Brewers, winemakers, and related workers	200
Coachpainters	200
Workers below ground	200
Telegraph and radio operators	200
Valets and related workers	200
Civil, structural, and municipal engineers	200
Judges, advocates, barristers, and solicitors	200
Barmen	200
Hairdressers, manicurists, and beauticians	200

As *Table 1* indicates, there are very large differences between the occupational risk of liver cirrhosis, which is highly associated with excessive drinking. Many of the high-risk occupations included in the table have already been discussed in relation to occupational studies or patients known to treatment agencies.

A discussion of the data in *Table 1* reviewed occupational mortality ratios for liver cirrhosis for men aged fifteen to sixty-four between 1959 and 1963 (Donnan and Haskey 1977). The 1961 data, when first published, had shown company directors to have the highest SMR (2,200). This is not shown in *Table 1* for the following reasons: Donnan and Haskey revealed that this SMR was spurious. First, the ratio was calculated on the basis of a mere twenty-two cases. Second, it appears that some of those classified after death as company directors probably were not (Donnan 1978). It would be interesting to know exactly what these men were. Even if they were not really directors, they may have been small businessmen whose evident high risk is in itself a matter worthy of attention. Donnan and Haskey delete brewers, barmen, judges, and hairdressers from the original 1961 list and add commercial travellers and various types of labourer (Donnan and Haskey 1977: 22). They interestingly present data concerning which occupational groups had significantly *lower* than average liver cirrhosis mortality ratios. These are shown in *Table 2*.

Table 2   Low-risk groups: male liver cirrhosis mortality (England and Wales 1959-63)

Occupational group	Standardized mortality ratio
Managers in building and contracting	11
Printing press operators	14
Office cleaners, window cleaners	25
Agricultural workers	29
Construction workers	33
Teachers	44
Carpenters and joiners	48
Machine tool setters, setter-operators	50
Fitters, machine-erectors, etc.	75

'Easy access to alcohol is a common factor in several of the occupations with high SMRs such as publicans and innkeepers, cooks, hotel keepers and restauranteurs. The stress of the occupation or its environment may influence men to drink, for example, insurance brokers and medical practitioners. Other occupations involve absence from home and thus isolation; or pressure from colleagues may encourage drinking if no alternative recreation is available (ships' officers and ratings, members of the armed forces, actors and commercial travellers and so on).

(Donnan and Haskey 1977: 23)

Donnan and Haskey suggest that while the low-risk occupations listed in *Table 2* may have genuinely low liver cirrhosis rates, this may be because men with drinking problems are excluded from such jobs.

Occupational liver cirrhosis mortality data for 1970 to 1972 were published during 1978 (Office of Population Censuses and Surveys 1978: 145). *Table 3* shows that there have been some changes since 1959 to 1963. The main change has been the increase in SMR values of some occupations.

Table 3 High-risk groups: liver cirrhosis mortality (England and Wales 1970-2)

Occupational group	Standardized mortality ratio
Publicans, innkeepers	1,576
Deck, engineering officers and pilots, ship	781
Barmen, barmaids	633
Deck and engine room ratings, barge and boatmen	628
Fishermen	595
Proprietors and managers, boarding houses and hotels	506
Finance insurance brokers, financial agents	392
Restauranteurs	385
Lorry drivers' mates, van guards	377
Cooks	354
Shunters, pointsmen	323
Winders, reelers	319
Electrical engineers (so°described)	319
Authors, journalists, and related workers	314
Medical practitioners (qualified)	311
Garage proprietors	294
Signalmen and crossing keepers, railways	290
Maids, valets, and related service workers	281
Tobacco preparers and products makers	269
Metallurgists	266

The 1970 to 1972 statistics are accompanied by the following comment:

'Cirrhosis of the liver ... has commonly been associated with high alcohol consumption and inadequate diet. Not surprisingly therefore, barmen, publicans and innkeepers as well as fishermen, deck and engineering officers and deck and engine room ratings, all units with high alcohol consumption, feature among the occupations with the highest mortality from this cause. For some of the occupations with high rates for cirrhosis of the liver, high alcohol consumption probably preceded the adoption of the occupation which was taken up because it afforded access to alcohol as well as providing the basic amenities of life such as board and lodging. For others, the occupation entails the separation of men from their homes, offering limited alternative opportunities for recreation.

That authors, journalists, medical practitioners, and finance and insurance brokers should be among the occupations with the highest mortality from cirrhosis probably reflects quite different circumstances. Men in these professions often accept high alcohol consumption and inadequate diet as a natural consequence of the demands of their work. Alternatively, their social habits may reflect their reactions to the stress or pressures of this type of work.

Such links between occupation and alcohol are not new. More than 250 years ago Ramazzini remarked on the lethargy of men working in the distilleries of Modena and early decennial supplements commented on the drinking habits of workmen in certain trades. Farr commented that, "The majority of the publicans and the greater part certainly of wine merchants are temperate and as the mortality of the whole trade is high the mortality of the intemperate among them must be excessive. Death by delirium tremens is a low kind of suicide".'

(Office of Population Censuses and Surveys 1978: 145)

The high rate of alcohol-related mortality in the drink trade has been evident ever since records were kept. Wilson's classic study *Alcohol and the Nation* included a chapter on this subject which concluded in relation solely to inn- and hotel-keepers that:

'Reviewing the figures of occupational mortality since 1860, it seems certain that the excess mortality among males (only) recorded as engaged in this trade has been not less than from 80,000 to 90,000 deaths. These figures do not include the excess mortality among other members (male and female) of the considerable army of persons engaged in this trade and liable to the temptations offered by alcohol.'   (Wilson 1940: 218)

The United States National Office of Vital Statistics (1961) produced a report that included information about some occupations with high liver cirrhosis mortality rates. These included barmen, waiters, canteen workers, transport workers (except railwaymen), cooks, and musicians. These findings are broadly similar to those relating to England and Wales.

Population surveys

Far less is known about 'normal' drinking habits than about alcoholics known to treatment agencies. A few sample surveys have been carried out which indicate that there are differences in the drinking behaviour of different social groups. While these do not reveal *occupational* differences, they do indicate differences between status groups such as manual and non-manual workers.

Cahalan and Room (1972), reviewing two national probability samples of American drinking habits and alcohol-related problems, found that heavier drinking and drinking problems were more common amongst lower-status males. Cahalan and Cisin (1966) also noted that, even so, amongst men aged twenty-one to thirty-nine, those in higher-status occupations were especially likely to be heavy drinkers.

Three British studies also produced results which are relevant to occupations. These were all based upon self-reported alcohol consumption data collected from random samples. Edwards, Chandler, and Hensman concluded from a survey of 408 males and 520 females in a London suburb that: 'The general statement can ... be made that more class I and II women are heavier drinkers and class I and II men are lighter drinkers than respondents in other classes' (1972: 76). A national survey of Scottish drinking habits which collected data from 1,613 males and 840 females concluded like Cahalan and Room (1972) that the heaviest drinking section of the adult population was young working class males (Dight 1976). In fact this study concluded that 30 per cent of the alcohol reportedly consumed by the sample during the week preceding interview had been drunk by a mere 3 per cent of those interviewed. This 3 per cent consisted largely of young male manual workers. Dight found also that the proportion of regular drinkers was greater amongst higher income groups (both males and females). She also found that amongst the extremely *low* income group (presumed to be pensioners) alcohol consumption was high

(Dight 1976: 19). Another Scottish survey collected self-reported alcohol consumption data from four towns: Ayr, Glasgow, Aberdeen, and Inverness. Altogether 874 males and 1146 females were interviewed. This study concluded that, while non-manual workers were more likely than manual workers to drink alcohol, the latter were far more likely to be heavy drinkers. In other words, manual workers appeared more likely to be either abstainers or heavy drinkers, while non-manual workers were more likely to be light drinkers (Plant and Pirie 1979). 'Social class' may be defined in many ways. It is of a different order from the *occupational factors* discussed throughout this chapter. Even so, it is important to note that broad categories of employment probably are influenced by the educational levels, home backgrounds, etc. of individuals in certain jobs.

As Chapter 3 will indicate, sample surveys such as these produce, at best, dubious results. Even so, evidence is consistent that there are considerable social-class differences in people's drinking habits. This fact is compatible with the evidence previously described that occupational groups of differing levels of status and with other variations in character have widely differing rates of alcoholism.

Explanations

As the preceding review has indicated, a great deal has been written about the link between alcoholism and different occupations. Only a small part of the total literature has been described, even though this summary probably gives a good indication of the scope of this work. A number of important qualifications are necessary which will be expanded in the following chapter in the elaboration of some of the problems encountered in alcoholism research. First, most studies of specific occupations have been carried out in isolation from similar information about the population in general. While they make the case that alcoholism is prevalent amongst doctors or servicemen, only a minority use control groups in order to discover whether the noted prevalence is really unusual. Descriptions of alcoholics known to agencies are invariably unrepresentative and usually reflect biases related to the specific agency. Sample population surveys have not yielded detailed information, even though they show many general differences in alcohol use or misuse. Probably the best indicator, even though it is only one

possible outcome of excessive drinking, is the liver cirrhosis mortality rate. Even this, as indicated in Chapter 1, is of very limited use
in determining the prevalence of alcoholism. It does have the merit
of having a wider coverage than either single occupational studies or
data from treatment institutions, and relates to specific occupations
which population surveys generally do not. Considering the various
types of information together, it appears that some occupations do
have far greater alcoholism rates than others for several reasons:

'Willis (1973) comments: "Surveys of alcoholics indicate that
some occupations do carry a high risk of alcoholism. These include
employment in the liquor trade and occupations where alcohol is
used as a business entertainment. Possibly a kind of selection
may operate in that people who have beginnings of an alcohol
problem may consciously or unconsciously choose such jobs.
There are some occupations which encourage easy relief from a
high level of tension by the ready availability of alcohol for entertainment purposes."

Hitz (1973) observes: "It may be that some occupations are
attractive to heavy drinkers because there is more tolerance of
heavy drinking and, by implication, less likelihood of the
worker's drinking getting him into trouble on the job."

Mellor (1967) makes a similar statement: "Occupations which
facilitate drinking by reason of the cheapness or easy availability
of alcohol, are associated with an increased prevalence of alcoholism. Certain occupations, with a high prevalence, have a tradition of heavy drinking to which beginners are introduced during
their novitiate." '   (Plant 1978:313)

Roman and Trice (1970) have made an important contribution to
discussions of why some jobs have especially high alcoholism rates.
They have suggested the following nine risk factors which may be
applicable to some high-status occupations, and which may foster
excessive or deviant drinking. These factors have been summarized
by Archer (1977: 18):
'Lack of visibility:
1 jobs in which production goals are nebulous;
2 flexible work schedules and output permitting the exercise of
   an individual worker's option;
3 jobs which are remote from the purview of supervisors and
   work associates.

Stress factors stemming from the absence of structural work:
4   work addiction;
5   work role removal and occupational obsolescence;
6   job roles novel to the organization.

Absence of social controls:
7   job roles which require drinking as part of work role perform-
     mance;
8   job roles in which one's deviant drinking benefits others in
     the organization;
9   Mobility from a highly controlled job status in which heavy
     drinking is practised to release tension into a job status which
     is also stressful but in which social controls are absent.'

Archer comments that risk factors for lower-status jobs are less
apparent, and refers to possibilities such as job satisfaction, insecurity of employment, danger, and unpleasant working conditions.

> 'Ironically, the general thrust of such arguments is that the
> source of much of the job discomfiture that may contribute to
> alcohol and drug dependency among lower status workers lies in
> the absence of the very work-role features which Roman and
> Trice have found to be possible precursers of alcohol abuse by
> persons in high status jobs.'   (Archer 1977: 19)

Archer, reviewing American findings, concluded that there is
little clear evidence linking work-role stress factors and alcoholism,
although some studies have indicated such a link (Hochwald 1951;
Strayer 1957).

From the studies reviewed in this chapter, eight 'risk factors' are
evident. Some apply only to certain occupations, but do, collect-
ively, explain why such disparate occupations have high alcoholism
rates. The main factors suggested are:

(a) *Availability of alcohol*:   Where alcohol is accessible during
    working hours. This is relevant to alcohol production and
    distribution, and to jobs in which 'entertaining' is common-
    place such as with business executives, commercial travellers
    (e.g. Wilson 1940; Frank *et al.* 1967; Kolb and Gunderson
    1977).
(b) *Social pressure to drink*: Where there is strong encourage-

ment by fellow workers to participate in heavy drinking. This is suggested as relevant to such groups as servicemen, seamen, commercial travellers, and workers in the drink trade (e.g. Brun-Gulbrandsen and Irgens-Jensen 1967; Carney 1963; Carney and Lawes 1967; Gwinner 1976; Kolb and Gunderson 1977; J.I.F. 1947; Rose and Glatt 1961; Wallinga 1956;).

(c) *Separation from normal social/sexual relationships*: Where jobs take individuals away from home for a long time or spending an unusual length of time away from the opposite sex. This factor applies to travelling jobs such as commercial travellers, seamen, servicemen, and to certain types of businessmen. The case of female domestic servants described earlier in this chapter is another example (Straus and Winterbottom 1949) (e.g. Donnan and Haskey 1977; Gwinner 1976; J.I.F. 1947; Long *et al.* 1977).

(d) *Freedom from supervision*: This parallels the 'lack of viability' suggested by Roman and Trice (1970). A review of alcoholism and employment by Murray (1975) suggested that the absence of supervision may be a risk factor for company directors and general practitioners. This factor could also apply to people in other high status or travelling jobs, such as judges, lawyers, and commercial travellers (e.g. Hughes 1975).

(e) *Affluence/poverty*: The survey of *Scottish Drinking Habits* (Dight 1976) found that regular drinking was associated with affluence and with low income. It is possible that the high purchasing powers of some occupations such as company directors and medical practitioners may increase their likelihood of becoming excessive drinkers (Hughes 1975; Murray 1976). Obversely, poverty may give people a particularly great need to use alcohol to dim harsh realities.

(f) *Collusion by colleagues*: The study by Roman and Trice (1972) indicated that in certain occupational positions an individual's alcoholism may be covered up, or even fostered. This has also been indicated in relation to the medical profession (Edwards 1975) and in relation to the protective paternalism of service life (Gwinner 1976).

(g) *Strains and stresses*: Many jobs have their own characteristic pressures and problems. The 'invincibility ethos' of the medical profession is a good example (Talbott *et al.* 1976). The dangers and constraints of military life or of seafaring, especially trawling, are probable factors. Those in the theatre and entertainment experience considerable insecurity of employment, and often spend long periods 'resting' between jobs. Doubtless company directors, doctors, commercial travellers, and most, if not all, high-risk jobs have particular, special pressures that could lead people to need consolation or relaxation through heavy drinking. Such pressures are widely referred to in the literature, but are difficult to single out in general terms.

(h) *Pre-selection of high-risk people*: The eighth factor that emerges as a possibility from this review is that high-risk jobs attract unusual or alcoholism-predisposed people. Several writers have suggested that jobs such as seafaring, the armed forces, or some of the professions attract or recruit people who are already excessive drinkers or who are especially likely to become such (e.g. Arner 1973; Brun-Gulbrandsen and Irgens-Jensen 1967; Office of Population Censuses and Surveys 1978; Rose and Glatt 1961).

Clearly there does not appear to be any one factor that leads obviously to high alcoholism rates amongst occupational groups. Several factors could well combine in some cases, while in others a single one alone might be relevant. Perhaps the most important question to be answered is whether high-risk jobs *attract* people predisposed to become alcoholics, or whether they simply *create* alcoholics through their work situations. It is this question to which the study described in Chapter 4 to 7 is primarily directed.

3 Problems of research

Limitations of evidence

It is not known how many 'problem drinkers' or 'alcoholics' there are in any society, or even what quantities people drink. This sad situation exists because our means of collecting information are all very limited and partial. Most of them are enormously biased and leave a great deal to be desired.

In order to produce an acceptable profile of the drinking habits or alcohol-related problems of a social group, one has to piece together a jigsaw. There are several sources of information available, and one may adopt numerous research strategies to achieve different objectives. Even if one uses several methods, the picture remains incomplete and uncertain. There have, in the past, been attempts to produce neat generalizations about the prevalence of alcoholism in the community (Jellinek 1951; Ledermann 1956). Such generalizations have optimistically assumed, first, that we have dependable information about drinking habits and alcohol-related problems and, second, that, even if our information was this good, populations in different places or at different times conformed to the same pattern. In fact, in the real world, things are not that conveniently simple (Duffy 1977).

Evidence about drinking patterns: sources and limitations

(a) *Surveys*: Much of our information about drinking habits is derived from surveys which collect *admissions* of what a sample of people report that they drink. Most surveys have been relatively small-scale affairs, seldom exceeding at most 2,000 to 3,000 interviews. Most have relied upon self-reporting of drinking habits. Surveys, often based upon records such as the Electoral Register, invariably exclude important subgroups within the population, such as the homeless, people in institutions (such as hospitals and hostels), and vagrants, all of whom may be of especially great interest. Few surveys have been done which have achieved coverage of whole national populations. Most have been confined to small groups, such as students, or to single, small geographical areas. It has been shown that there are very great local variations in drinking habits, even between towns 40 to 50 miles apart (Plant and Pirie 1979). It is not justified, therefore, to generalize from single towns or districts to other areas. Even the *Family Expenditure Survey*, often referred to as a source of information about drinking habits, does not cover the whole population, and is limited by wives' misconceptions about their spouses' alcohol consumption. Surveys seldom validate the authenticity of the information they collect, and usually rely upon answers elicited during a single, brief interview. Whenever other evidence is available by which to judge survey results, it is apparent that people generally under-report what they drink. A review of this deficit suggested that surveys only reveal 20 to 70 per cent of national consumption (Pernanen 1974). Moreover, it seems likely that under-reporting is especially great amongst those who are either known alcoholics or heavy drinkers (Popham 1970; Schmidt 1972). In effect, surveys provide us with a distorted indication of people's drinking habits rather than with the true picture. If only a small percentage of people in the population are heavy drinkers or alcoholics, and if these are the least truthful when asked about their drinking, surveys are a poor representation of patterns of alcohol consumption.

(b) *Total alcohol consumption*: Government departments record the annual production of various types of alcoholic beverages. In Britain these figures probably give a good impression of the total amount of alcohol consumed. In many countries 'official' production figures omit important home brewing or distilling which may be unrecorded or even illegal. Some countries import and export much of their alcohol. And in some countries wine produced is not all drunk, but may be used as fuel (Kreitman 1976). It is probable that in many non-industrialized countries the 'official' figures of alcohol production tell us relatively little about actual consumption. We can only guess at the size of this inaccuracy.

(c) *Average consumption*: It is possible to work out supposed average consumption by using the Census as a measure of population, and government production figures as an index of the total amount of alcohol consumed. Even this begs a lot of issues. We do not know what percentage of the population do not drink at all, and any results depend upon what definitions of drinker and non-drinker are used. It is usually found that about 10 to 15 per cent of those aged eighteen and over in British surveys do not drink (Dight 1976), but there is certainly a lot of geographical variation, and some areas have a higher percentage of teetotalers than others (Plant and Pirie 1979). Even if one knows what average alcohol consumption is in a country, one still does not know the variance that exists between drinkers. Two countries may have the same average consmption and very different patterns of drinking.

(d) *Purchases*: Some researchers have recorded purchases of alcoholic drinks (de Lint and Schmidt 1971). While there is probably a high correlation between purchasing drinks and consuming them, it cannot be assumed that purchasing is synonymous with consumption.

Evidence about alcohol-related problems: sources and limitations

(a) *Surveys*: Some surveys have been confined to investigating drinking habits (Dight 1976). Those which have also examined alcohol-related problems (e.g. Cartwright *et al*. 1976; Edwards *et al*. 1972; Saunders and Kershaw 1977) are subject to the limitations described above, of under-reporting, incomplete coverage, and bias. Under-reporting is probably especially great amongst those who really do have alcohol-related problems.

Most of the available information about alcohol-related problems comes from 'official agencies' dealing with either law enforcement or providing treatment.

(b) *Law enforcement*: Governments publish figures of people arrested, reported, or convicted for alcohol-related offences such as drunken driving, breach of the peace, being drunk and disorderly, etc. These figures depend upon (i) the law at any given time or place and (ii) police policy in enforcing the law. Many people who infringe laws are not detected and reported. Police behaviour and legal definitions vary between countries, and at different times. The number of people convicted of drunken driving depends as much upon how many people can afford cars as upon the number of drunks in the community. The number of drink-related offences recorded in any given year may depend upon the size of the police force having to enforce the law, and upon the scale of other forms of crime. Only a proportion of law breakers are recorded in crime statistics (Hood and Sparks 1970: 11-45).

(c) *Clinical records*: Clinical records describe people receiving treatment for alcoholism. There is clear evidence that only a minority of problem drinkers or alcoholics are identified or helped by 'official agencies', possibly as few as 11 to 25 per cent (Edwards *et al*. 1973). The members of many professions, such as general practitioners, are known to identify only a minority of the alcoholics they encounter (Wilkins 1974). The picture is further confused by the fact that many people who are treated for alcohol-related problems evidently contact more than one agency, so that records are confused by duplication (Delahaye 1977). The proportion of problem drinkers seeking help from agencies depends upon what agencies are available, how these are advertised, and upon the stigma in any social group attached to being labelled as 'alcoholic'. These things vary from place to place and further complicate comparisons.

(d) *Liver cirrhosis mortality*: It has often been conceded that one of the best indicators of the prevalence of alcoholism is the rate of mortality due to liver cirrhosis. First, this only tells us how many dead alcoholics there are, not how many living ones. Second, the relationship between liver disease and alcoholism varies from one country to another, and varies over time. Only a minority of identified alcoholics appear to develop liver cirrhosis. Nevertheless, roughly 70 per cent of liver cirrhosis mortality in Britain is related to excessive drinking.

(e) *High-risk groups*: A person's chances of developing drinking problems depend upon the social resources available to cope with stresses. Rich people will have fewer financial problems than poorer people if they are heavy drinkers. A judge is unlikely to have an industrial accident if drunk, while a machine operator is highly vulnerable. As the discussion in Chapter 2 indicated, some people, such as servicemen, commercial travellers, and publicans, are exposed to more pressures to drink heavily than others. Some people are more likely to have their alcohol-related problems detected and to be recorded by official agencies than are others. International comparisons are very dubious since methods of data recording and definitions of 'problem' and 'alcoholism' vary considerably.

Implications for survey research

From the preceding discussion it is evident that surveys of drinking behaviour and alcohol-related problems are imperfect instruments and their results need to be interpreted with great caution. Because of the inherent problems of bias and under-reporting, precise percentage results are undependable. Because of the considerable local variations that exist in drinking habits and in the prevalence of alcohol-related problems, a study of a single group of people in a single area is not a basis for sweeping general conclusions. These qualifications are important ones and need to be borne in mind when considering the investigation described in the following chapters.

On the positive side, there are important justifications for using survey methods. First, existing documentary information about drinking habits and alcohol-related problems is very limited, being largely confined to people known to official agencies. Observational methods can be, and have been, used to investigate the *public* alcohol consumption of only relatively small groups of people (Cutler and Storm 1975; Kessler and Gomberg 1974; Plant *et al*. 1977; Sommer 1965). While it is possible to use observation to produce interesting *qualitative* information (Cavan 1966), this has largely been confined to public behaviour and is necessarily impressionistic if not limited to extremely small study groups.

Surveys are the logical method to use in collecting information about private or not readily observable behaviour from relatively large groups of people. Because of the limitations of precise percentage findings about drinking habits and alcohol-related problems, it is probable that the most useful results will be produced when some form of comparison is carried out. This may involve either a longitudinal survey which monitors changes in the same group of individuals at different times, or comparison of one subgroup with another. While one should not place excessive trust in a survey description of a single group at a single time, the differences between two groups, or of one group at different dates, may be revealing.

4 Cause or effect?

Outline of the study

Aims. There is little doubt that heavy drinking and alcohol-related problems are far more common in some occupations than in others. As shown by the review in Chapter 2, this has been discussed widely and many theories have been expounded. While most of the speculation has been concerned with how certain occupational settings *cause* workers to drink more heavily and to encounter more problems in consequence, another theory has been suggested. This relates to the possibility that high-risk occupations may *attract* people who are either already heavy drinkers or who have alcohol-related problems or who are predisposed to become heavy drinkers. This is an interesting and important 'chicken and egg' question: do high risk occupations attract heavy drinkers, or do they create them? The following chapters describe a study that was undertaken to achieve the two following primary aims:

(1) To ascertain whether a high-risk occupation recruits workers who are already heavy drinkers or alcoholics, or who appear especially predisposed to become such.

(2) To examine the effect upon workers' drinking habits and alcohol-related problems in consequence of working in a high-risk occupation.

Method. The high-risk industry selected for this investigation was the drink trade, specifically brewing and distilling.

In order to examine possible selection factors, new recruits to alcohol production firms were compared with a control group of broadly similar workers newly recruited to other industries not known to have a high alcoholism rate. The study was carried out in the Edinburgh area.

Edinburgh, capital of Scotland, is a major educational, banking, and insurance centre with a population of more than 450,000. Several manufacturing industries are located in the Edinburgh area, including alcohol production. One reason for the choice of Edinburgh as the study area was the fact that alcohol production is only one of many possible occupations available. If the study had been carried out in the Highlands and Islands of Scotland, the range of alternatives to working in the drink trade (distilling) would have been reduced and this may have distorted results considerably. The 1971 Census showed that only 2.5 per cent of the economically active males in Edinburgh were engaged in brewing or distilling.

The co-operation was enlisted of five local manufacturing companies: two breweries and one distillery, and two other (control-group) firms. All recruited relatively large numbers of male manual workers from Edinburgh and the surrounding Lothian Region. All five companies operated similar shift systems, and had comparable wage levels. In addition, all prohibited the consumption of alcohol at work. This last point is important since some breweries and distilleries allow workers to drink a free daily allowance of alcohol, a practice sometimes known as 'dramming' or 'the pundy'. None of the three alcohol-production firms included in this study retained this system, and they had a general policy of disciplining, or even dismissing, workers caught drinking on the job. With the full consent of management and trade unions, newly recruited male manual workers were interviewed consecutively until study groups of 150 alcohol producers and 150 controls had been obtained. Most of the 300 respondents were interviewed within a few days of commencing employment and none had been in their new jobs for longer than three months.

Information was collected by interviewing each man privately at work using a standardized schedule which was administered by a trained interviewer. The main schedule used for the first interview contained 129 separate questions. Of those, 102 had been used previously in three earlier studies (Dight 1976; Edwards *et al*. 1972; Plant 1975). The other twenty-seven questions were devised for this study. The schedule included questions on the following topics (see *Appendix Ia*):

1 Description of current job
2 Previous record of employment
3 Educational background
4 Smoking habits
5 Drinking habits
6 Assessment of what constituted 'light' and 'heavy' drinking
7 Experience of alcohol-related problems
8 Drinking at work
9 Perception of workmates' drinking habits
10 Parental drinking habits
11 Drinking habits of wife, fiancée, or girlfriend
12 General biographical data, including birthplace, age, marital status, criminal record, recent bereavement, income.

The schedule was initially pre-tested with six members of Edinburgh University Psychiatry Department, then with six male manual workers living in a largely working-class suburb of Edinburgh. No major problems being evident, the fieldwork procedure was piloted among twenty male manual workers at a Stirlingshire distillery. Each of these men was interviewed by the researcher who first used the standardized schedule and, second, elicited data in a less formal manner to check the reliability (consistency) of replies. While this type of interview probably produces distorted results, as noted in Chapter 3, there was no reason to believe that the validity of the alcohol producers' replies was markedly different from that of the control group's replies. This view is reinforced by the fact that neither alcohol producers nor controls were officially permitted to drink at work.

Design.   The study was longitudinal in design (*see Table 4*). This was necessitated by the second primary research aim, to monitor changes in drinking habits and alcohol-related problems after entry into a high-risk occupation. Data collection was arranged as follows:

1 Initial full-length interview, as described, with 150 alcohol producers and 150 controls.

2 *One year* after completion of all initial interviewing, it was attempted to re-interview every third respondent (fifty alcohol producers and fifty controls) using a shortened version of the original interview schedule (see *Appendix Ib*).

3 *Two years* after the completion of initial interviewing it was attempted to re-interview all 300 respondents using the shortened version of the interview schedule.

Table 4   Timetable of the study

---

1   *September to October 1974*
Design of study
Compilation of interview schedule

2   *November 1974*
Pre-testing schedule

3   *December 1974 to January 1975*
Piloting schedule
Arranging with five companies to carry out fieldwork

4   *March to December 1975*
Initial interviewing of 150 alcohol producers and 150 controls

5   *March to December 1976*
One year follow-up interviewing of one third of respondents (N 100)

6   *September 1977 to April 1978*
Two/three-year follow-up of all respondents (N 300)

The purpose of this follow-up design was to establish at the outset the relative proportions amongst the alcohol producers and controls who were a) light drinkers, b) heavy drinkers, or those with alcohol-related problems, and c) those who were initially light drinkers but who appeared, for biographical reasons, to be predisposed to become heavy drinkers or to develop alcohol-related problems. The follow-up over two years was intended to discover how the study group's initial pattern of drinking and alcohol-related problems changed as men remained in their original jobs or left them. It was anticipated that over a two-year period contact would be lost with some respondents. Since it was decided that at least 100 alcohol producers and 100 controls should, if possible, be followed up two years later, 150 of each were interviewed initially to allow for depletion or 'attrition' of the cohort.

In view of the limitations of surveys, indicated in Chapter 3, one is well-advised to pay little attention to baseline data describing drinking habits or rate of alcohol-related problems of a single group of people. The design of the present study enabled two types of comparison to be made: first, the alcohol producers could be compared with the controls; second, baseline data collected during initial interviews could be compared with changes over time elicited during follow-up interviews. It is these comparisons, rather than any general statement of prevalence, that is largely the concern of the following description.

5 The new recruits

The initial interviews were carried out between March and December 1975. Three hundred men were interviewed, 150 alcohol producers and 150 controls. In addition to these, eight individuals refused to be interviewed, of whom six were alcohol producers. Workmates of some of those who refused volunteered to interviewers that these individuals had avoided the interview because they wished to conceal the fact that they were heavy drinkers.

Interviewing was all carried out during working hours at the respondents' work places in private rooms made available by company officials. Probably the high response rate of 97.4 per cent is attributable to the fact that interviewing was in company time, rather than the individual's spare time. Interviewing was carried out by the researcher helped by five other males of whom two were social scientists and two were nurses in the Unit for the Treatment of Alcoholism at the Royal Edinburgh Hospital.

Background characteristics of the study group

All of those interviewed were male manual workers. While the alcohol producers and controls were very similar in terms of their general social background, the alcohol producers included a significantly* higher proportion of younger, unmarried men.

Age. As *Table 5* indicates, seventy-four of the alcohol producers were aged twenty-five or under compared with only forty-nine of the controls. This was an important difference and all results are analyzed taking into account the greater youthfulness of the alcohol producers.

Table 5 Age

Age	Alcohol producers	Controls
Under 25	74	49
26 to 35	50	59
36 and above	26	42
Total	150	150

Marital status. Consistent with these age differences, fifty-eight of the alcohol producers were unmarried compared with only thirty-seven of the controls. One interesting difference *not* explained by age was the fact that the alcohol producers were significantly less likely than controls of the same age to be either separated or divorced. Overall nine alcohol producers and twenty-one controls had such broken marriages.

The two sub groups were not significantly different in relation to education, birthplace, father's occupation, or rate of previous employment in the drink trade or alcohol-related jobs.

Education. As one might expect from a group of largely unskilled and semi-skilled manual workers, virtually none had any kind of formal educational qualifications. Only twenty-three of the alcohol producers and thirty-two controls had any qualifications, either GCE Ordinary levels or apprenticeships.

Country of birth. The great majority of both subgroups were born in Scotland. Altogether 135 of the alcohol producers and 122 of the

---

* In order to simplify presentation, statistical tests are not included in this book. Whenever 'significant' differences are mentioned, this indicates that X^2 (with Yates' Correction) or other tests indicated at least 95 per cent probability of differences $(P < .05)$

controls were Scots born. Only three alcohol producers and twelve controls were born outside the United Kingdom.

Father's occupation. Of the 300 respondents, 264 reported that their fathers had been, like they themselves, manual workers. Only sixteen alcohol producers and twenty controls reported that their fathers were non-manual workers.

Previous employment in alcohol-related jobs. Following from speculation that recruits to the drink trade might be people particularly disposed to seek out such work it was interesting that the alcohol producers did not differ from the controls in this respect. Altogether, fifty-one of the alcohol producers and fifty-three controls had formerly worked in alcohol production or distribution or in other jobs with high alcoholism rates. More of the controls had been in the armed forces, but this difference was due solely to age. Taking age into account, those in either subgroup who had previously worked in high-risk jobs were not drinking more than those who had not.

Poor employment records. All respondents were asked about their previous jobs and rate of job change over the two years before recruitment. The alcohol producers were significantly more likely than the controls to have had poor work records. More had experienced frequent job changes (that is five or more jobs during the previous two years) or had previously been in better jobs. Altogether thirty-one of the alcohol producers, compared with only twelve controls, had such poor employment histories. *This was an important difference between the two subgroups, consistent with the view that the alcohol producers were a more disturbed group, some of whom entered the drink trade while in the process of slithering down the social scale.*

Reasons for applying for job. The alcohol producers were significantly more likely than the controls to report that they had applied for their present job due to the company's reputation as a secure source of employment, nineteen compared with only five. In addition, the alcohol producers were also significantly more likely than controls to report that they had been attracted to their new jobs by 'good pay levels'.

It is possible that in the Edinburgh area certain brewing and distilling firms have a reputation for security. Certainly the drink trade often weathers economic depressions better than many other manufacturing industries. In fact both of the control group firms were very prosperous throughout the period covered by this study, and were working at full capacity. The fact that alcohol producers were more likely than controls to attribute their attraction to their new jobs to wage levels is not a reflection of differences in their income. Controls were in fact as well paid as alcohol producers of the same age. The only obvious difference between the working conditions of the two subgroups was that the controls were significantly more likely than the alcohol producers to be working on a shift rota, 112 compared with only eighty.

Drinking patterns

Each respondent was asked, first, whether he did drink alcohol, and, if so, to give a precise account of what he had drunk during the seven days preceding the interview. While a week's diary such as this may not be completely typical there is evidence that most people report that it is a good indication of what they usually drink (Dight 1976). In order to clarify this point each respondent was asked whether or not his previous week's drinking was typical, and, if not, what a typical week would be. The main measure of consumption used in this study is the total previous week's consumption. This is calculated on the basis of units of alcohol, each equivalent to either half a pint of beer, lager, cider, etc., or to a single glass of spirits or wine. These units contain approximately 1.0 centilitre or 7.9 grammes of alcohol.*

Previous week's consumption. As anticipated, 84.7 per cent of those interviewed reported that their previous week's alcohol consumption had been fairly typical of what they usually drank in a week.

* The alcohol content of beverages varies considerably. A single glass of whisky of the usual Scottish measure of $\frac{1}{5}$ of a gill contains about 1.0 centilitre. Some lager contains 2.2 centilitres in half a pint, while some beers contain only 1.0 centilitre. There is no standard measure for a glass of wine, although this could easily vary between 0.6 and 2.2 centilitres.

Abstainers and non-drinkers. Only three men, all control-group workers, reported that they never drank alcohol. In addition eleven alcohol producers and twenty-nine controls reported that they had not consumed any alcoholic drinks during the previous week. There was no significant difference between the proportion of younger alcohol producers and controls who had not drunk alcohol in the previous week, six out of seventy-four compared with nine out of forty-nine. Even so, alcohol producers aged twenty-six and above were significantly more likely to have drunk alcohol in the past week than comparable controls, seventy-one out of seventy-six with only eighty-one out of 101.

Drinking levels. The average amount of alcohol reportedly consumed during the previous week was significantly higher amongst the alcohol producers than amongst the controls, 33.1 units compared with only 21.4 units. These differences are shown in *Figure 1*.

Figure 1   PREVIOUS WEEK'S CONSUMPTION

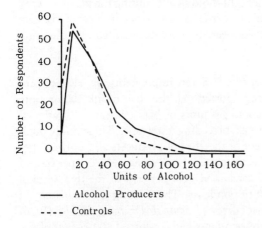

────── Alcohol Producers

- - - - Controls

As already noted, there were important age differences between the two subgroups. These are taken into account in *Figure 2*, which indicates the average levels of self-reported alcohol consumption of respondents divided into three age groups.

As *Figure 2* shows, amongst respondents aged under twenty-five and between twenty-six and thirty-five, the alcohol producers were

Figure 2   AVERAGE PREVIOUS WEEK'S CONSUMPTION

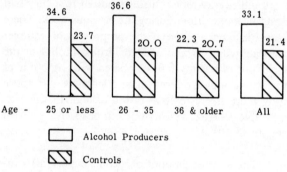

significantly heavier drinkers than the controls. While older alcohol producers had a slightly higher average consumption than controls, this difference was not significant. Even so, the evidence clearly shows that amongst respondents up to the age of thirty-five average consumption amongst the alcohol producers was more than 45 per cent higher than amongst the controls. Overall, the alcohol producers had drunk 35.4 per cent more alcohol during the previous week than the controls. This is a striking difference in view of the fact that the alcohol producers were only newly recruited into the drink trade.

Heavy week's consumption.   Seven respondents, six alcohol producers and one control, reported that they had drunk 100 or more units (equivalent to about 50 pints of beer or nearly 4 bottles of whisky) during the week preceding interview. These individuals represented 4.0 per cent of the alcohol producers and only 0.7 per cent of the controls. Between them these seven men, 2.3 per cent of all those interviewed, consumed 11.0 per cent of the total alcohol consumed by the 300 respondents. This finding is reminiscent of Dight's findings in her survey of *Scottish Drinking Habits* (1976) that 3 per cent of her respondents had consumed 30 per cent of the alcohol drunk by her sample. It is also consistent with Dight's study that all seven heavy drinkers in this study were aged thirty-five or less.

Highest daily consumption.   It is of great importance not just how much alcohol a person drinks in a week, but how much is consumed at a single time, for example, during a day or an evening 'session'. To clarify this distinction, two men may have identical total weekly consumptions, but entirely different drinking habits and quite different experiences of alcohol-related problems. If a man drinks fifteen pints of beer between 7 pm and 10 pm on a Saturday night he will risk experiencing many problems attributable to drunkenness. A man who spreads his fifteen pints evenly over the week, drinking only two or three pints a day, will not be so vulnerable (Edwards *et al.* 1972). In order to examine drinking habits from a second perspective, alcohol consumption is also examined in relation to the highest daily amount each respondent reported drinking. The results, divided into three age groups, are shown in *Figure 3*.

Figure 3   HIGHEST DAILY CONSUMPTION

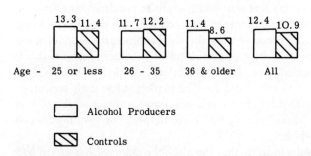

The average highest daily consumption of the alcohol producers was 12.4 units. This was slightly, but not significantly, higher than the average of the controls, 10.9 units. As *Figure 3* indicates, only amongst those aged thirty-six and older was the highest daily consumption of the alcohol producers significantly greater than the controls. Amongst younger men the differences were slighter. In fact, controls aged twenty-six to thirty-five had a marginally higher consumption than the alcohol producers.

Dight's survey of *Scottish Drinking Habits* (1976) indicated that the typical pattern is for people to concentrate their drinking at weekends. The results of this study are similar. Alcohol consumed on the single day of greatest consumption accounted for 37.4 per cent of the alcohol producers' weekly consumption. Amongst the controls the highest single day's consumption accounted for 50.9

per cent of their weekly total. This difference is explained by the fact that the alcohol producers, having a generally higher level of weekly consumption than the controls, were more likely to have drunk alcohol on several days. One important reason for this, discussed below, was the fact that many were able to drink during the week at work. The results of the present study were consistent with Dight's conclusions that most drinking occurs at weekends, especially on Saturdays. In addition, those who drink less are most likely to drink only at weekends, while heavier drinkers are more likely also to drink during the week (Dight 1976: 111-23). It was apparent, for many of the men interviewed in this study, that a high proportion of their drinking involved fairly heavy 'sessions'. Usually these were at weekends, and often drinking clearly led to some degree of intoxication. This is a very different thing from having a casual pint or two.

The heaviest daily drinkers.   Fifty-eight respondents, twenty-nine alcohol producers and twenty-nine controls, reported that on one day during the previous week they had consumed twenty or more units (ten pints of beer or its equivalent in wines and spirits). Of these, seventeen, five alcohol producers and twelve controls, had consumed thirty or more units. The highest single daily consumption was reported by a thirty-year-old control group worker who had drunk fifty units (twenty-five pints of beer, or just under two bottles of whisky).

These results indicate that the alcohol producers as a group had consumed more alcohol in the previous week than the controls, and had a slightly higher maximum daily intake. Even so, the same number of controls had consumed at least ten pints in a single day, and rather more controls than alcohol producers had reportedly consumed more than fifteen pints in a day. Clearly, one may use two definitions of 'heavy drinkers', one relating to total weekly consumption, the other to heavy drinking on a single day. If the former definition is preferred, there were more heavy drinkers amongst alcohol producers; if the latter is preferred, both groups were the same at the 20 unit level, but the controls had more 'heavy drinkers' at the 30 unit level.

Assessment of heavy drinking.   The great majority of those interviewed stated that they were primarily beer and lager drinkers. Few drank wine, and spirits were typically reserved for special occasions or at least were consumed only at weekends. This is certainly not consistent with the popular stereotype of the whisky-drinking Scot, which is certainly more relevant to the Highlands than to the Edinburgh area. There are very great local differences in patterns of local alcohol consumption in different parts of Scotland (Dight 1976; Plant and Pirie 1979).

Respondents were asked to state their assessment of the quantities of beer and whisky a man would need to drink in a week to be counted as a heavy drinker. There was no significant difference between the alcohol producers' and the controls' average estimates of what constitutes heavy whisky consumption: 3.8 and 3.7 bottles respectively.

Consistent with their own generally higher weekly beer consumption, the alcohol producers had a higher average assessment of the threshold of heavy beer consumption than the controls, 61.7 pints compared with only 55.7 pints. This difference was not significant. Even so, the alcohol producers were significantly more likely than the controls to assert that a heavy beer drinker would have to consume at least eighty pints a week, thirty-six compared with only eighteen.

The influence of the new job on drinking habits

Respondents were asked whether or not they had begun drinking more since starting their new jobs. The alcohol producers were significantly more likely than the controls to report that they had started to drink more, thirty-two compared with only six.

Eighty-one of the alcohol producers compared with only one of the controls admitted that they drank illegally at work. In fact there is reason to suggest that on-the-job drinking was more widespread in the control group than the single admission indicates. On the first night of the fieldwork at a control-group company, interviewers observed the following request on the workers' notice board:

> 'Will employees please refrain from the practice of throwing ring-tops from beer cans into the production line? We are currently being sued by three public health authorities because such rings have been discovered in packets of … [the firm's product].'

In addition management and security staff reported that one of their major problems, especially with night shift workers, was of preventing people from smuggling drinks into work premises, or arriving for work while drunk. This was a *control-group* company, not a brewery or distillery.

In the light of such evidence, it is probable that more than eighty-one of the alcohol producers and one control-group worker did sometimes drink at work. Seventy of the eighty-one alcohol producers who reported such drinking stated that they were able to drink virtually whenever they liked, and that most of their workmates also availed themselves at will of whatever alcoholic drinks were accessible. These results clearly substantiate the view that when a group of men enter a work situation where alcohol is available, many will increase their consumption accordingly.

Perception of workmates' drinking habits

Respondents were asked whether any of their workmates were heavy drinkers, and, if so, what proportion. These questions prompted more reticence than any others in the interview. Some men stated that they had not been in their new jobs long enough to be able to comment on other workers' drinking habits. Others clearly thought that it would have been a betrayal of confidence to comment, and did not reply for this reason.

The alcohol producers were far more likely than the controls to supply information on this topic, ninety-five compared with only thirty-nine. This could be interpreted as indicating that the alcohol producers were less inhibited about this subject, since they had not been in their new jobs any longer than the controls. The ninety-five alcohol producers who commented on what proportion of their workmates were heavy drinkers made a significantly higher assessment than the thirty-nine controls, 37.2 per cent compared with only 29.3 per cent. Clearly the alcohol producers were not only more willing to discuss their workmates' drinking habits, but were much more likely to perceive themselves as working in an environment characterized by a lot of heavy drinking. This difference is especially striking since, as indicated above, the alcohol producers had a rather more liberal definition of what constituted 'heavy drinking' than the controls. Altogether twenty-nine of the alcohol producers reported that more than half of those with whom they worked were heavy drinkers. Such an assessment was made by only three control-group workers.

Perceived harm

Thirty-seven men reported that in their view at least some of their new workmates suffered due to drinking. The alcohol producers were significantly more likely than the controls to say this, twenty-six compared with only eleven. What was perhaps even more striking than this difference was that eleven of the alcohol producers stated that they worked alongside men who, in their assessment were alcoholics. None of the control group made such a statement. The most common types of problem reportedly observed were domestic and financial, which were noted by twelve men. Other problems were job inefficiency combined with 'family troubles' (three), accidents (three), aggression (two), drunkenness at work (one), and marital disharmony (one). Clearly the alcohol producers were both especially likely to perceive alcohol-related problems at work, and to notice what they regarded as 'alcoholism'. When asked during interview to elaborate upon these comments, men typically reported some of their workmates indulging in relief drinking and drinking continuously at work: 'Three of the group start drinking as soon as they arrive. Some have to drink to stop their hands shaking'; 'Some of the older men are in a bad way. I know a few who drink all day long. Everybody knows about them and they never get into trouble. People cover up.'

Several personnel officials conceded that sometimes a man's excessive drinking would be tolerated. Sometimes it was believed that he had been a good worker, whose 'downfall' was simply a tragic occupational hazard. One manager explained:

> 'In coal mining you get the black lung. In our industry it's alcoholism. It happens to a few just because they have been in the job too long. When this happens we assign them to easy jobs. One of our warehouses is full of guys like that. We call it the "Elephants' Graveyard".'

Tobacco smoking

There was no difference between the smoking habits of the two subgroups. One hundred and nine of the alcohol producers and 120 of the controls reported that they sometimes smoked tobacco. In addition there was no significant difference between the proportions of heavy smokers in either subgroup. Forty-seven of the alcohol producers and fifty-six controls reported smoking more than twenty cigarettes daily or three ounces of tobacco weekly. These similarities were not affected by age.

Alcohol-related problems

Respondents were asked the following eighteen questions:

(a)   Have people annoyed you by criticizing your drinking?

(b)   Have you ever had difficulties at work because of your drinking?

(c)   Has your doctor ever advised you not to drink as much as you do?

(d)   Have you ever spent more money than you ought to on drink?

(e)   Have you ever had trouble or quarrels with family or friends because of your drinking?

(f)   Have you ever had health problems because of your drinking?

(g)   Have you ever had financial problems because of your drinking?

(h)   Have you ever been in a road accident (as driver or pedestrian) because of your drinking?

(i)   Have you ever been in other accidents (home/work) because of your drinking?

(j)   Have you ever had a drink first thing in the morning to steady your nerves or to get rid of a hangover?

(k)   After drinking have you found your hand shaky in the morning?

(l)   Have you ever arrived late at work due to a hangover?

(m)   Have you ever missed a day's work due to a hangover?

(n)   After drinking have you ever found you can't remember the night before?

(o)   Have you ever gone without a drink for a period to prove you can do so?

(p)   Do you ever find that when you start drinking you can't stop?

(q)   Have you ever had special medical treatment for drinking?

(r)   Have you ever 'heard' or 'seen' things due to drinking?

Altogether, 227 of the 300 respondents reported that they had experienced at least one of these alcohol-related problems. The alcohol producers reported an average of 2.8 problems each compared with an average of 3.5 for the controls. Both in relation to any single one of these problems and to the total number experienced, there was no significant difference between the two subgroups. In addition there was no significant difference between the numbers of alcohol producers and controls who had experienced ten or more problems. None of the older alcohol producers had experienced this number although seven of those aged thirty-five or less had done so. This difference was consistent with the higher level of alcohol consumption amongst younger men. Ten of the controls had experienced ten or more problems, but this was not related to age.

While there were no major differences between the problem scores of the alcohol producers and controls, *Table 6* indicates that a large number of male manual workers have experienced alcohol-related problems. While the alcohol producers did not appear to be more likely than the controls to have experienced alcohol-related problems, a minority in both such groups had clearly experienced sufficient difficulties to be regarded as an 'at risk' group.

The high problem-scorers

Seventeen men, seven alcohol producers and ten controls, reported having experienced ten or more of the problems listed below. With the exception of the absence from this group of alcohol producers aged forty-five and above, they were unremarkable for age and other biographical characteristics. They were, however, significantly more likely than other respondents to report that their highest day's alcohol consumption during the previous week had been at least twenty units. Seven of the eleven, 63.6 per cent, had drunk this much compared with only 17.0 per cent of the rest of the men interviewed. This association is not surprising since most of the eighteen problems are connected with high alcohol consumption during a relatively short period of time, such as a single day. Three of these men, one alcohol producer and two controls, reported that their highest daily consumption in the previous week had been forty-six, thirty-two, and fifty units respectively. Their average problem score was 12.3.

Table 6   Experience of alcohol-related problems

Problems in rank order	Alcohol producers	Controls	Total
	N	N	N
1 Had spent too much money on drink	64	70	134
2 Had gone without drink for period to prove ability to do so	48	64	112
3 After drinking have been unable to recall previous night	53	54	107
4 Had experienced trouble or quarrels due to drinking	32	42	74
5 Had been annoyed by people criticizing own drinking	34	36	70
6 Hand had been shaky after drinking	33	33	66
7 Had arrived late at work due to hangover	30	29	59
8 Had drunk first thing in morning to steady nerves / remove hangover	23	30	53
9 Had missed day's work due to hangover	19	29	48
10 Had experienced alcohol-related financial problems	15	24	39
11 Had been advised by doctor to drink less	9	25	34
12 Sometimes unable to stop once started drinking	8	24	32
13 Had experienced alcohol-related health problems	13	16	29
14 Had experienced alcohol-related work problems	7	14	21
15 Had been in alcohol-related road accident	9	8	17
16 Had 'seen or heard things' due to drinking	5	9	14
17 Had received medical treatment due to drinking	3	9	12
18 Had been in alcohol-related accident at home or work	6	3	9

Physical damage

Respondents were asked if they had ever suffered from the following conditions associated with alcohol misuse: stomach ulcers, liver disease, or TB of the chest.

Stomach ulcers: The alcohol producers were significantly less likely than the controls to report that they had a stomach ulcer, ten compared with twenty-three. This difference was attributable to the higher average age of the controls. While it is notable that 11.0 per cent of those interviewed had had a stomach ulcer, several more volunteered that they had experienced gastritis (inflamed stomach). Some stated that they associated gastritis with heavy weekend drinking. Since this was not included in the initial interview, no data are available, but it was decided to add this item to the two follow-up interviews.

Liver cirrhosis: Three alcohol producers and one control reported that they had suffered from liver cirrhosis. All conceded that this had probably been due to heavy drinking when they were younger.

TB of the chest: Four of the alcohol producers and one control had had TB. There was no evidence to connect this fact with heavy drinking.

Altogether, seventeen of the alcohol producers and ten of the controls reported having experienced at least one of these physical problems. Of these, three men, one alcohol producer and two controls, had suffered from two of the three symptoms. These differences were not statistically significant, and physical damage was not related to age.

Alcohol-related convictions

Fifty-seven of the alcohol producers and sixty-one controls had been convicted of at least one criminal offence. Minor motoring infringements were not included. This difference was not significant, neither was there a significant difference between the numbers of alcohol producers and controls who had been given a custodial or suspended sentence, related to more serious offences.

The control group were significantly more likely than the alcohol producers to have been convicted of an offence directly related to alcohol misuse, such as drunken driving, drunk and disorderly, or breach of the peace. Twenty-nine controls and twelve alcohol producers reported such convictions. It is possible that men with alcohol-related convictions are less likely to apply for, or are screened out of, the drink trade. Certainly nobody with such a conviction related to motoring would be appointed as a driver. Alternatively, men engaged in brewing and distilling may have been more likely than controls to deny more serious alcohol-related problems such as convictions.

Perception of own drinking

Respondents were asked which of the four following statements came closest to the way they felt about their own drinking:

1 I wish I could afford to drink more than I do now
2 I'm perfectly satisfied with the amount I drink now
3 I sometimes feel I should drink a bit less than I do
4 I would definitely like to cut down the amount I drink.

Twenty-two respondents, eleven alcohol producers and eleven controls, reported either that they sometimes felt they should drink less (fifteen) or that they would definitely like to cut their drinking down (seven). While there was no difference in this respect between the two subgroups, it is notable that out of a group of new recruits to brewing and distilling firms, eleven or 9.3 per cent had doubts about the amounts they were drinking, of whom four or 2.7 per cent stated that they definitely wanted to drink less. This minority had in fact entered a work situation where their wish to drink less could scarcely be facilitated by the ready availability of alcohol combined with an ethos of tolerance of, even encouragement for, heavy drinking.

Previous drinking habits

Population surveys commonly indicate that people generally drink heavier during their teens and twenties than thereafter. For many this can simply be explained by marriage, which can often lead to reduced alcohol consumption (Cahalan and Room 1972). Ninety-nine of the 300 respondents, 33.0 per cent, reported that they had been, in the past, either slightly heavier (thirty-nine) or much heavier (sixty) drinkers. Many of these men commented that their heavy drinking had occurred when they were single or in the armed forces and that they had drunk much less since getting married or taking on family responsibilities. There was no significant difference between the number of alcohol producers and controls who reported that they had once been slightly heavier drinkers, nineteen and twenty respectively. The controls were significantly more likely to report that they had formerly been much heavier drinkers, fifty-eight compared with only twenty-two. This difference is due to the higher average age of control-group workers. These findings support existing evidence that men do often moderate their drinking as they pass from their twenties to their thirties and forties. It is also clear that, because the alcohol producers in this study were younger than the controls, more were still in their youthful, single, heavier drinking phase.

Family drinking problems

There were no significant differences between the proportions of alcohol producers and controls reporting that either their parents or their girlfriends, wives, etc. had experienced alcohol-related problems. Altogether thirty-three of the alcohol producers and thirty-nine controls reported that one or both parents had experienced problems due to their drinking. Of these, twenty-one reported that both parents had been problem drinkers, thirty-eight reported that the problem drinker had been their father and three stated that it had been their mother. It is an interesting insight into the family backgrounds of manual workers that 19.0 per cent of all those interviewed reported coming from a home where at least one parent had encountered alcohol-related problems. These respondents referred to marital strife, violent arguments, and money problems. Such incidents had clearly been a long-term feature of the early family lives of many of the respondents.

In addition, five of the alcohol producers and thirteen of the controls reported that their girlfriend, fiancée, or wife had also encountered some form of alcohol-related problem. All eighteen men reported that their female partner's drinking had led to heated arguments.

Age of partner

It has been suggested that male alcoholics are likely to marry much older women (Kessel and Walton 1974: 107). It has been speculated that if this predisposition is related to heavy drinking, the alcohol producers might be more likely than the controls to have older female partners. In fact there was no difference in this respect between the two subgroups. Eleven alcohol producers and thirteen controls reported having older partners, while eleven alcohol producers and sixteen controls had younger partners.

Parasuicide (*attempted suicide*)

Twelve men, three alcohol producers and nine controls, reported that they had at some time taken an overdose. While these numbers are too .small to warrant statistical analysis, they do indicate that the alcohol producers were not any more likely than the controls to have made a parasuicidal act. All twelve parasuicides were aged thirty-five or younger. This is consistent with the general youthfulness of parasuicides in Edinburgh (Kreitman 1977).

Psychiatric illness

There was no significant difference between the proportion of alcohol producers and controls who reported that they had at some time 'had trouble with their nerves', seventeen and twenty-three respectively. Reported psychiatric illness was not related to age.

Conclusions from the initial interview

The two subgroups were composed of very similar people in relation to birthplace, educational background, and social class. Both the alcohol producers and the control group were engaged in broadly similar types of work and were receiving similar rates of pay. The initial interviews indicated that there were some important differences between the two subgroups, not in relation to family background, but in relation to occupational histories and to drinking habits. These six differences were:

1 The alcohol producers were significantly more likely than the controls to have poor records of previous employment.
2 The alcohol producers aged thirty-five and under were significantly more likely than comparable controls to have a high week's total alcohol consumption.
3 The alcohol producers made a significantly higher assessment than the controls of what constituted heavy beer drinking.

4 The alcohol producers were significantly more likely than the controls to report drinking more since starting their new jobs.

5 The alcohol producers were significantly more likely to report that their workmates were heavy drinkers, and to make a higher estimate of what proportion were in this category.

6 The alcohol producers were significantly more likely than the controls to report that some of their workmates suffered due to drinking. In particular, only some of the alcohol producers stated that some of those with whom they worked were alcoholics.

The initial interviews also produced some negative results. In many ways the two subgroups were not different. It is of interest that although the drinking habits of the alcohol producers differed from those of the controls, the former did not appear to have suffered more alcohol-related problems. This may have been due to the fact that the alcohol producers were newly recruited to the drink trade. What is of interest is what happened to them later on. This is discussed in Chapters 6 and 7. The initial interviews indicated that a minority of men in both subgroups had encountered a variety of alcohol-related problems, and that these were related to the general pattern of drinking relatively large amounts of alcohol on only a few occasions, mainly at weekends. Many men described their own drinking, making it clear that for some, drinking was synonymous with getting drunk. (The phrase 'having a good drink' was frequently employed to explain this phenomenon.)

These results need to be interpreted with caution. As explained in Chapter 3, such surveys probably produce distorted results. It is not possible on the basis of this information to conclude how many, if any, of those interviewed, were 'alcoholics' or even potential alcoholics. Nevertheless, the preceding analysis does indicate that the alcohol producers, even at recruitment, were far more likely to be heavy drinkers, and appeared to have increased their alcohol consumption since entering a work environment where this was possible due to availability and social support.

6 One year later

One year after they were initially interviewed, a third of the original sample, fifty alcohol producers and fifty controls, were sought for reinterview. Every third man on the initial list was included in this follow-up. Fieldwork was carried out between March and December 1976. Since sixty-one of the 100 men had left their original employment, fieldwork was far more complicated and time consuming than when all had originally been interviewed at their places of work. Forwarding addresses had to be visited, and often a series of clues followed up to secure interviews. At the first interview each respondent had supplied at least one forwarding address. Most of these were sufficient, but some men had lost contact even with their closest relatives and could not be traced. In the end, eighty of the 100 respondents were successfully reinterviewed. In addition, five refused to be reinterviewed and fifteen were not contacted. Response one year after the initial interviews was 94.0 per cent of those contacted, but only 80.0 per cent of all those sought. Interviewing was carried out in private by four trained male fieldworkers using a shortened and amended version of the original schedule (see *Appendix 1b*). Each interview took ten to fifteen minutes.

Current employment status

As *Table 7* indicates, only twenty-two of the alcohol producers and

Table 7 Current employment status

Status		Alcohol producers	Controls
With same company ⎱	in same	22	17
With different company ⎰	subgroup	—	15
Changed subgroup		10	2
Unemployed		8	6
Total		40	40

seventeen of the controls were still working for the company where they were originally interviewed. Ten of the alcohol producers were currently working in control-group firms which did not have a high alcoholism rate. In addition, fifteen control-group workers had moved to other firms unconnected either with the drink trade or high alcoholism rates. One control-group worker had moved into alcohol production and a second had joined the Merchant Navy, a 'high-risk' industry. These two men were reclassified as having changed subgroup. Eight of the alcohol producers and six controls were out of work. These changes enabled us to examine the following three situations:

(a) Remaining in alcohol production
(b) Leaving alcohol production
(c) Entering alcohol production or other high-risk jobs.

In addition, an analysis is presented of what features differentiated those men who refused to be interviewed or who could not be contacted.

Reasons for changed employment

Nine of the forty-one men who had left their original jobs reported that they had been dismissed. Five of these were alcohol producers and four were control-group workers. One of the dismissed alcohol producers reported having been discharged because he was caught in a state of intoxication at work. He had been drinking illegally on company premises. Altogether thirteen alcohol producers and nineteen controls reported having left their original companies through choice. Three of the alcohol producers stated that they had left their jobs in brewing or distilling because they were worried that their drinking was getting out of hand. All three reported being influenced by the ready availability of alcohol at work and by strong pressures to conform to their workmates' habitual heavy drinking. One of these three, a driver, left due to fears that he would lose his driving licence if breathalyzed. The other two, brewers, were influenced in their decisions to leave by their wives, who had warned them that they were 'verging on alcoholism'. One of these wives had threatened to leave her husband unless he found a 'drier' job and reduced his drinking accordingly. In addition, one man left alcohol production because he had developed liver cirrhosis. A second alcohol producer left work to serve a prison sentence.

The stables

Twenty-two, 55.0 per cent, of the alcohol producers and thirty-five, 87.5 per cent, of the controls successfully reinterviewed had remained in the same type of work. A comparison of these men in either subgroup is presented to indicate what changes had occurred in their self-reported drinking habits and alcohol-related problems. For the purposes of this discussion, such men are referred to as 'stables' regardless of whether they had changed companies within alcohol production and other high-risk jobs or within control-group type employment.

Table 8 The stables : age

Age	Alcohol producers	Controls
Under 25	10	12
26 to 35	9	12
36 and above	3	8
Total	22	32

Consistent with differences noted at initial interview, the alcohol producers were more likely than the controls to be younger (see *Table 8*). Age is taken into account in presenting the following results.

Drinking patterns

Two important questions are: first, how much had changed in a year, and, second, how did the alcohol producers compare with the controls? The original average week's total consumption of the fifty-four stables one year earlier is shown in *Figure 4*.

Figure 4 THE "STABLES": INITIAL WEEK'S CONSUMPTION

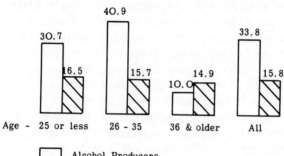

One year later there had been a considerable change in the amount either subgroup of stables had consumed, as shown in *Figure 5*.

Figure 5 THE "STABLES": WEEK'S CONSUMPTION ONE YEAR LATER

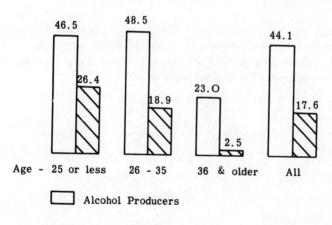

Percentage change. The average week's consumption of the

twenty-two alcohol producers at initial interview was 33.8 units, more than twice that of the thirty-two controls, 15.8 units. One year later the overall consumption of the alcohol producers had increased by 30.4 per cent, while that of the controls had only risen by 11.4 per cent. In fact, there was no significant difference between the percentage increases in consumption of alcohol producers and controls aged thirty-five or less. What was striking was that amongst the three alcohol producers aged thirty-six and over there had been a 130 per cent increase in consumption. Amongst their eight counterparts in the control group there had been an equally dramatic *decrease* in consumption of 83.2 per cent (i.e. from 14.9 units to 2.5 units). Not only were the alcohol producers drinking much more than the controls, but all of them reported having drunk some alcohol during the previous week, while eleven of the thirty-two controls, 34.4 per cent, reported they had not. Only amongst the few older men had there been a major change between the two subgroups. Overall the average consumption ratios of the alcohol producers:controls had changed from 2.1:1 to 2.5:1. This means that while the alcohol producers were drinking 30.4 per cent more than one year previously, their consumption had only increased by 16.0 per cent in relation to the control group. Amongst all three age groups the alcohol producers were drinking far more than the controls.

Change in units consumed. While the percentage increases amongst those aged thirty-five or less in either subgroup were similar, there was a considerable disparity in the actual increase in units consumed. This is shown in *Table 9*.

Table 9   The stables : average change in units consumed

Age	Alcohol producers	Controls
25 or less	+ 15.8	+ 9.9
26 to 35	+ 7.6	+ 3.2
36 or above	+ 13.0	—12.4
Total	+ 10.3	+ 1.8

+   indicates increase
—   indicates decrease

As *Table 9* indicates, in each of the three age groups the alcohol producers had increased their week's consumption by at least 4.4

units more than the controls. Due to the previously much higher average consumption of the alcohol producers, the 'real' increases were not great in percentage terms. The consumption changes shown in *Table 9* are an important reminder that the average alcohol producer at one year follow-up was drinking 10.3 units extra, while the average control-group worker was only drinking 1.8 units extra.

Assessment of heavy drinking

Consistent with the results of the initial interviews, the alcohol producers had a significantly higher average assessment of the amount of beer a man would have to consume in a week to be a heavy drinker. The alcohol producers' average estimate was 62.3 pints compared with only 43.0 pints for the controls. Also consistent with the initial results, alcohol producers and controls did not differ significantly in their estimates of the amount of whisky a man would have to consume in a week to be a heavy drinker, 2.8 bottles and 3.0 bottles respectively. As already remarked, the different assessments of heavy beer drinking broadly reflected the heavier beer consumption of the alcohol producers. An interesting development was that increased alcohol consumption amongst the control group had been reflected by fifteen of the thirty-two controls increasing their estimate of heavy beer drinking. This had not happened to the same extent among the alcohol producers, only six out of twenty-two of whom increased their assessment in comparison with the previous year. One interpretation of this is that the alcohol producers upon recruitment to their jobs already had a very liberal interpretation of what constituted heavy beer drinking. This assessment was considerably higher than their general level of consumption either initially or one year later. Their subsequent 30.4 per cent increase in alcohol consumption had not, therefore, necessitated any major shift in thinking about 'heavy' drinking. The control group, however, were lighter drinkers whose average assessment of heavy beer drinking, 43.0 pints, was safely above their own average week's alcohol consumption, 15.8 units initially and 17.6 units one year later. As lighter drinkers with a more restrictive view of 'heavy' drinking, a relaxation of their assessment may have been a natural rationalization of the fact that they were generally drinking rather more than one year before.

Perceptions of workmates' drinking habits

As at the original interview, the alcohol producers were more likely than the controls to report that some of those with whom they worked drank much more than they themselves did, nineteen out of twenty-one compared with twenty-four out of thirty-two. In addition, eighteen of the twenty-two alcohol producers, 81.8 per cent, reported that they worked alongside heavy drinkers compared with only twenty-one of the thirty-two controls, 65.6 per cent. Of the thirty-nine men replying in this way, the alcohol producers made a significantly higher average estimate than did the controls of the percentage of their workmates drinking heavily, 29.1 per cent compared with 18.2 per cent. In view of the alcohol producers' far more liberal definition of what constituted 'heavy' beer drinking, this difference is even more striking.

Perceived harm

The alcohol producers were still significantly more likely than the controls to assert that some of those with whom they worked suffered because of their drinking, ten out of twenty-two compared with only six out of thirty-two. Two of the alcohol producers and one of the controls reported that they worked alongside at least one man whom they regarded as an alcoholic. Both of the alcohol producers stressed that they knew *several* men who indulged in relief-drinking immediately upon arrival at work each day. Job inefficiency, marital discord, gastritis, and financial problems were also cited.

Alcohol-related problems

While both subgroups had increased their alcohol consumption over one year, neither had significantly altered the number of problems they had experienced from the list of eighteen items (see *Appendix 1b*, question 13). There was no significant difference between the proportions of alcohol producers and controls who had increased or decreased their problem scores or whose scores remained the same, as shown in *Table 10*.

No individual reported any significant change in his problem score. As *Table 10* indicates, six alcohol producers said that they

Table 10 The stables : changes in problem scores

Problem score	Alcohol producers	Controls
Increase	13	15
Decrease	6	10
Same	3	7
Total	22	32

had experienced fewer problems at second interview than they had at first interview. This probably indicates more about the doubtful reliability of some of the problem questions rather than about the individual's current relevant problems. It may, however, indicate that the problems were less salient.

Physical damage

Seven alcohol producers and eight controls reported that they had suffered from gastritis, a stomach ulcer, liver cirrhosis, or TB.

> *Gastritis*, the most common of these four disabilities, was reported by seven alcohol producers and eight controls. The alcohol producers were more likely to report having suffered from gastritis, but not significantly so.
>
> *Stomach ulcers* were reported by three alcohol producers and one control. All four were amongst those reporting that they had also had gastritis. Of these, two alcohol producers reported that their ulcers had developed and been diagnosed since entering the drink trade.
>
> *Liver cirrhosis*, or rather 'liver trouble', was reported by two of the alcohol producers. Both men stated that this had been diagnosed by their family doctors since their initial interviews. In neither case had a clear diagnosis of liver cirrhosis been made. Both men were still drinking in spite of their doctors' orders to the contrary.
>
> *TB of the chest* was reported by one control-group worker. He had contracted this illness several years before being included in this study.

All twelve of those with gastritis linked it with their drinking. Several commented that this was a commonplace complaint amongst their friends who 'liked a good drink'. Since this item had not been included in the original interview it cannot be inferred that gastritis had developed since recruitment. Even so, it is striking that, out of twenty-two men employed in alcohol production for only one year, two had developed stomach ulcers and two had developed some form of liver disorder.

Alcohol-related convictions

Nine of the twenty-two alcohol producers and nine controls reported that they had been convicted of a criminal offence during the year since their original interview. Of these, seven alcohol producers and four controls reported that at least one of these new convictions was alcohol related. All seven of the alcohol producers had been convicted for offences specifically related to drunkenness, either breach of the peace (six) or drunken driving (one). Two of the controls had been recently convicted of drunken driving. Two had been convicted of theft offences, which both attributed to the fact that they had been drinking. These numbers are too small to warrant a statistical comparison, but it is of importance that in the first year of their employment in the drink trade seven out of twenty-two had been convicted of an alcohol-related offence. An eighth man had been convicted of possessing cannabis.

Separation / divorce

There was no significant difference between the numbers of alcohol producers and controls who had become separated or divorced since being interviewed one year earlier, two and three respectively. There was no evidence relating these marital rifts to drinking habits.

Absenteeism

Nine alcohol producers and ten controls reported that they had taken at least one day off work during the previous month. Of these, two of the alcohol producers and one control reported that their absences had been due to hangovers following heavy drinking sessions at the weekend.

Admission of alcohol-related problems

While respondents were asked about the specific alcohol-related problems already discussed, it was considered important whether or not they themselves perceived such things as difficulties. To this end, each man was asked: 'Has there ever been a period in your life when drinking has caused you problems?' Those answering in the affirmative were also asked: 'Is drinking causing you problems at present?'

There was no significant difference between the proportions of those in either subgroup reporting that they had ever experienced drinking problems or that they were currently experiencing such problems. Nine alcohol producers and nine controls stated that they had known a period in their lives when drinking had caused them problems. Only four alcohol producers and four controls reported that, in their view, they were currently experiencing problems. Most of those who reported having experienced specific difficulties such as accidents, financial problems, or alcohol-related convictions were not prepared to declare that 'drinking had caused them problems'. Such things were generally taken for granted and were not conceded to give cause for concern. Many respondents volunteered that minor social upheavals such as fights and argu- ments did not worry them, and some of those who had been convicted of offences such as breach of the peace or drunken driving made it clear that they had not been unduly perturbed by such things. Clearly many of those interviewed used a very different definition of 'problem' from that employed by the researcher. Much of this difference was attributable to a widespread acceptance amongst those men, alcohol producers and control group alike, that drinking meant getting drunk, and that many of the attendant consequences of drunkenness were both expected and accepted. They were all part of the game.

These results show clearly that settling into work in brewing or distilling had led to some notable changes; men were drinking more and were still especially likely to perceive their workmates as heavy drinkers or as suffering from drinking. While overall problem scores from the list of eighteen items remained unchanged, four of the twenty-two alcohol producers reported suffering from physical symptoms associated with heavy drinking which they did not have upon recruitment. In addition, a third of the alcohol producers had been convicted of an alcohol-related offence during their first year in the drink trade. These were the results of the preliminary follow-up of only a third of the study group. What happened to the complete group two years after initial interview is described in Chapter 7. Attention will now be focussed on what happened to those who left the drink trade and to those who entered it during the first year.

The leavers

Eighteen of the forty alcohol producers reinterviewed one year after first contact had left the drink trade. Ten of these were currently working in control-group type industries which did not have high alcoholism rates. A further eight were unemployed. There is clearly a major difference between continuing to work and being unemployed. Since it is of great interest to examine the effects of moving from a high-risk industry into lower-risk employment, these two subgroups of 'leavers' are examined separately.

Fourteen of the leavers were aged under twenty-five. Three were aged twenty-six to thirty-five and only one was over the age of thirty-six, as shown in *Table 11*.

Table 11   The leavers : age

Age	Working	Unemployed	Total
25 or less	8	6	14
26 to 35	2	1	3
36 and over	0	1	1
Total	10	8	18

Drinking patterns

In total contrast to those who had remained in the drink trade, those who had left it were generally drinking much less than when first interviewed. Twelve of the eighteen were drinking less than previously. Only five were drinking more. The overall changes in a week's consumption, related to age, are depicted in *Figure 6*.

As *Figure 6* shows, the eighteen leavers, both unemployed and still working, had *decreased* their consumption by an average of 35.5 per cent. While the numbers of those aged twenty-six or above (four) are too small to warrant statistical comparison, those aged twenty-five or less were drinking significantly less than when in the

Figure 6 THE "LEAVERS": CONSUMPTION CHANGES OVER
ONE YEAR

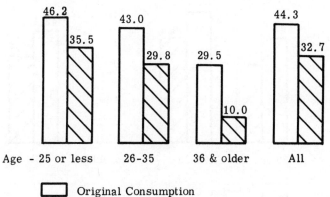

Age - 25 or less   26-35   36 & older   All

☐ Original Consumption

▨ Consumption One Year Later

drink trade one year earlier, and the overall decline is also
significant.

Not surprisingly, the eight leavers who were unemployed had
reduced their consumption by significantly more than the ten who
were still working, by 40.3 per cent compared with only 31.2 per
cent. This difference is understandable since the average unemployed leaver had a weekly income of only £21.37 compared with
£46.40 for those still in employment. It is likely, therefore, that the
real effect of leaving the drink trade is shown by *Figure* 7. The
greater decline in consumption shown in *Figure 8* is almost certainly
due both to departure from the drink trade and to greatly reduced
spending power.

The six younger unemployed leavers were still drinking quite a
lot, and had been even heavier drinkers upon initial interview.
Three of these men commented that while out of work they had
more time to spend in their local public bars, even if they could ill
afford to do so. In marked contrast, the six controls who were
currently unemployed had *increased* their average consumption by
92.8 per cent, from 19.7 units to 38 units. Of the six, one had
drunk the same amount as when interviewed one year earlier, two
had slightly decreased their consumption, and three had increased
their consumption. One man had increased his previous week's

Figure 7 THE "LEAVERS": THOSE STILL WORKING (N10)

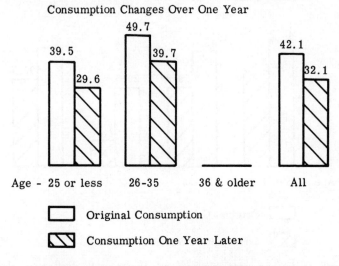

Consumption Changes Over One Year

Age - 25 or less   26-35   36 & older   All

☐ Original Consumption

▨ Consumption One Year Later

Figure 8 THE "LEAVERS": THE UNEMPLOYED (N8)

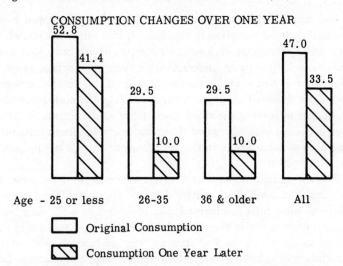

CONSUMPTION CHANGES OVER ONE YEAR

Age - 25 or less   26-35   36 & older   All

☐ Original Consumption

▨ Consumption One Year Later

consumption from 29.5 units (roughly 15 pints of beer) to 129.5 units (65 pints). Beyond doubt unemployment is a stressful and frustrating experience. It may be that for the controls unemployment involved an increase in pressure to drink, whereas for the

One year later 83

alcohol producers it led to relatively less change in such pressure.

The 35.5 per cent overall consumption decrease of the eighteen leavers is in total contrast to the 30.4 per cent increase in consumption of the stables who remained in the drink trade over the same period. It is also notable that those who had left the industry had, upon initial interview, been drinking more than their stable counterparts were at the same time, 44.3 units compared with only 33.8 (see *Figure 4*). These differences are partly explained by the youthfulness of the leavers (see *Table 11*). In addition, it could be that heavier drinkers, as indicated by the initial interview results, are more likely than others to change their jobs frequently. This possibility is supported by the fact that one of the leavers had been dismissed for drunkenness and three reported leaving in order to reduce their alcohol consumption.

Assessment of heavy drinking

Consistent with their reduced level of (mainly beer) consumption, twelve of the eighteen leavers had reduced their assessment of what level of drinking was required to be a heavy beer drinker. In addition, eight individuals had also reduced their assessment of what constituted heavy whisky drinking. The leavers' average estimate of the threshold of heavy beer drinking was only 28.9 units compared with 62.3 units estimated by the stable alcohol producers. Their estimate of heavy whisky drinking was the same as that of the stable alcohol producers, 2.8 bottles. In view of the fact that virtually all of those interviewed were largely beer or lager drinkers, their assessment of beer drinking probably had far more significance. There were no differences between those still working and the unemployed with regard to their assessments.

Alcohol-related problems

The leavers were significantly more likely than the stable alcohol producers to say that they had experienced fewer of the list of eighteen problems than they had reported at first interview. Twelve of the eighteen leavers gave this reply compared with only six of the twenty-two stables. Interestingly, seven of the eight leavers who were unemployed reported a fall in their problem score. The numbers of leavers are too small to warrant statistical comparison, but the unemployed, having reduced their consumption by 40.3 per cent, may have been prompted to regard such problems as less relevant. Clearly it is not logically possible for the number of problems these men had 'ever' experienced to decline. This indicates that answers to such questions were unreliable (inconsistent). In addition it may be that the twelve leavers reporting fewer problems at second interview than one year earlier were less conscious of such difficulties having left a work environment where their drinking habits were heavier.

It is also a possibility that people have a short memory for many alcohol-related problems and that this 'decline' indicated a real decline in *current* or recent problems.

Physical damage

Two of the eighteen leavers reported that they had sustained alcohol-related physical damage since being interviewed one year earlier. Both were currently unemployed. One man had developed a stomach ulcer, the second had developed liver cirrhosis. The former was continuing to drink (sixteen pints the previous week). The second had stopped drinking completely on his doctor's advice after the diagnosis of his liver cirrhosis. He had in fact been obliged to give up work altogether as he was very ill physically. Both men reported that their months in the drink trade had played a part in the development of their physical disabilities. Both had been drinking heavily before that, however, and described their entry into the drink trade as simply 'the straw that broke the camel's back'.

Alcohol-related convictions

Five of the eighteen leavers reported having been convicted of at least one alcohol-related criminal offence since their initial interviews. A sixth had been fined for possessing cannabis. Three of these men had been fined for breaches of the peace committed when they were drunk. One man had been fined both for drunken driving and for three acts of assault under the influence of drink. The fifth man had been obliged to leave his original alcohol-production job to serve a nine-month prison sentence for an assault which he reported had been committed while he was drunk. All five of those who had been convicted of alcohol-related offences in the past year reported having committed at least one of these offences while still in the drink trade. Two of these five men were unemployed.

Separation / divorce

One unemployed man reported having separated from his wife since the initial interview. He reported that this was unconnected with his drinking.

Admission of alcohol-related problems

None of the leavers conceded that they were currently experiencing any alcohol-related problems. Five reported that they had, in the past, experienced such difficulties, but that they were now drinking less and had resolved their earlier problems.

Those who had left the drink trade had thereafter significantly reduced both their alcohol consumption and their assessment of what constituted heavy beer drinking. Five of the eighteen leavers reported that they had left alcohol production for reasons directly connected with their drinking: three due to fears that they were drinking too much, one due to liver cirrhosis, and a fifth due to a drink-related prison sentence. Like the 'stable' alcohol producers, some of those who had left the drink trade had suffered either physical disabilities or had been convicted of offences due to their drinking.

The entrants

One man who was originally a control-group worker had, at second interview, moved into the drink trade. A second control-group worker had started work as a merchant seaman. Since the Merchant Navy, as described in Chapter 2, has a high alcoholism rate, this man's development is examined as if he were an 'entrant' to the drink trade.

The first of these men, aged forty-one, had been a very light drinker(one pint of beer a week) who had not encountered any alcohol-related problems at initial interview. One year later his weekly consumption had increased to 11 units (5 ½ pints of beer) and he still reported not having encountered any alcohol-related problems. This was not surprising in view of his low alcohol consumption.

The second man, aged twenty-five at first interview, provides an interesting case history. He had originally consumed only 10 units (5 pints of beer) during the week preceding his initial interview. Since then he had spent nine months as a merchant seaman, which was still his job one year later. He reported that during the previous week he had drunk 130 units (the equivalent of 65 pints of beer). He stated that he was regularly drinking a bottle of rum a day while at sea, and that his previous week's consumption was lower than usual because he drank less while at home in Edinburgh. He attributed the dramatic increase in his drinking to the fact that his two cabin-mates on board ship were heavy drinkers and he found it 'impossible' not to join in with their drinking. He reported that that during the nine months that he had worked at sea his problem score had risen from nine to fourteen. In addition, he had begun to suffer from persistent gastritis and had been in 'many' fights when drunk. These had led to his being disciplined for unruly behaviour by his ship's captain. He reported that upon returning home on leave two weeks earlier he had spent £60 on drinking in the first three days. He frankly conceded that his drinking was causing him very serious problems, and reported that he was 'addicted'. He stated that he had to drink continuously to 'feel right' and that he generally awoke each morning to experience acute shaking in his limbs. Over the past year he had had accidents on board ship due to drinking, had been unable to start work promptly due to hang-overs, had experienced amnesias and hallucinations. He asked the interviewer for advice about how to cope with his difficulties. Subsequently an appointment was made for him to meet a psychiatrist colleague, but he failed to put in an appearance on the day.

This is only the experience of two men, one of whom was still a very light, problem-free drinker. Even so, the case history cited above is an extremely good example of how greatly a man's drinking habits and alcohol-related problems may change after entering a new work *milieu*.

Non-response: who dropped out?

The major problem of a follow-up study such as the present one is that there is a risk that some of the original subjects will subsequently drop out for various reasons. As explained in Chapter 4, it had been anticipated that the original study group would, over time, become depleted. One year after they had been interviewed initially, five of the 100 men sought for reinterview refused to co-operate further with the study and a further fifteen could not be contacted. It is of importance to determine whether these men were identifiably different from those who were contacted and who agreed to be interviewed a second time.

The refusals

Three alcohol producers and two control-group workers refused to be reinterviewed. All had left their original employment, and were visited at their home addresses. Presumably the fact that the reinterview involved them giving up some of their own time rather than being carried out at work, as before, may have influenced their refusals. None of these five men gave any reason for refusing to co-operate further. One, an alcohol producer, was clearly 'high' on cannabis (which the interviewer smelt) at the time of refusal. Consequently he was revisited a few weeks later, but refused again and appeared to be very hostile.

All five of those who refused to be reinterviewed were young, the eldest being thirty-five. All were unmarried. Two had reported quite heavy alcohol consumptions the week before being interviewed, 54 units and 95 units respectively. The second one of these had a maximum daily consumption that week that was exceedingly high, 42 units, equivalent to 21 pints of beer or a bottle and a half of spirits. This man reported having experienced nine out of the eighteen alcohol-related problems and the other heavy drinker reported having experienced twelve. Two of the five refusers had been convicted of alcohol-related offences and a third had been convicted of possessing cannabis. Altogether three of the five refusers had convictions related to alcohol or illegal drugs and a fourth appeared to be quite deeply involved with illegal drug use. Two were certainly heavy drinkers who had experienced far more than the average number of alcohol-related problems.

The non-contacts

Seven alcohol producers and eight control-group workers were not recontacted. All fifteen had left their original employment and had moved away from their original addresses. One man had apparently deserted his wife and five had 'done moonlight flits', that is, they had left their previous addresses without bothering to pay their rent. A seventh man had last been heard of frequenting common lodging houses associated with extreme social deprivation. Extensive enquiries were undertaken to track these men down. Five had lost touch completely with their parents and a further five forwarding addresses had become completely derelict. They were all in depressed mining areas of West Lothian and Lanarkshire. These had very high unemployment rates and contained many houses and flats that had been vacated during the study period.

All seven of the alcohol producers and six of the eight controls were aged thirty-five or less. Three of the alcohol producers and one of the controls had drunk more than 50 units (25 pints of beer) during the week preceding their interview one year earlier. Six of the seven alcohol producers and two controls had been convicted of an alcohol-related offence such as breach of the peace (five), drunk and disorderly (one), drunk and incapable (one), or theft while under the influence of drink (one). In addition, one alcohol producer and one control-group worker had suffered from a stomach ulcer. While the numbers of non-contacts were too small to warrant statistical comparisons, it is clear that those who were alcohol producers were more likely than their counterparts who were reinterviewed to have been convicted of an alcohol-related offence. This is consistent with evidence from other studies indicating that those who drop out of follow-up surveys are often found to be more 'deviant' or disturbed than those who continue to be traced and co-operative (e.g. Cox *et al.* 1977). Altogether ten of the twenty men who either refused to be interviewed or were not contacted had been convicted of an alcohol-related offence. This was a significantly higher conviction rate than amongst the eighty men who were reinterviewed, of whom only twelve had reported having such convictions at their original interview. It appears fairly evident that those men not interviewed were a rather different group from those who were reinterviewed. The fact that the one-year follow-up produced only an 80 per cent response rate clearly limits the results. Even so, some very clear-cut findings were produced and these are summarized below.

Conclusions from one-year follow-up

The main conclusion was that some individuals had changed both their drinking habits and alcohol-related problems dramatically over a single year. These changes were clearly related to whether they had remained in the drink trade, had left it, or had joined it. These results showed that working in the drink trade had a significant impact upon men's drinking habits and, in consequence, upon their alcohol-related problems. One particularly striking discovery was that some men had left the drink trade in order to reduce the pressures to drink to which they were exposed. It has long been suspected that some people do take positive and successful action to resolve their drinking problems, and this is confirmed by the reinterviews. At a more general level the results indicate that remaining in, departure from, or entry into the drink trade made a 30.0 per cent difference in weekly alcohol consumption and often also changed perceptions of what constitutes heavy beer drinking. A disturbingly high proportion of those remaining in the drink trade for one year had experienced either physical damage or had been convicted of an offence related to alcohol. If this is an indicator of a more general or continued pattern, this is indeed a very alarming development. The main results of the one-year follow-up were:

1 Five of the eighteen alcohol producers who had left the drink trade had done so for alcohol-related reasons. Three of these left because they were worried about their drinking.

2 Those remaining in the drink trade had increased their weekly alcohol consumption by far more than those remaining in the control group.

3 Those remaining in the drink trade were more likely than those in the control group to have developed alcohol-related physical damage, although the numbers were too small to be significant.

4 There was no significant difference between stable alcohol producers and controls in relation to other problems or in changes of their assessment of what constituted heavy drinking.

5 Those who had left the drink trade had significantly decreased

their weekly alcohol consumption and their assessment of what constituted heavy beer drinking.

6 The leavers who were unemployed had reduced their consumption by more than those who were still working. This was probably due to their much lower incomes.

7 Only two men had entered the drink trade or other 'high-risk' employment. Both had greatly increased their weekly alcohol consumption and one had developed many new alcohol-related problems.

8 Those men who were not reinterviewed were significantly younger and were significantly more likely to have alcohol-related convictions than those who were reinterviewed.

One year was not a long time, yet some major changes had occurred. This was purely an interim follow-up intended to provide an indication of what to expect two years after the initial interviews. The results of the full-scale reinterview are described in the following chapter.

7 Two years later

Between two and three years after initially being interviewed all 300 respondents were sought for a final reinterview using the shortened, amended schedule (see *Appendix 1b*). Fieldwork was carried out between September 1977 and April 1978. Since many respondents had left their original jobs and home addresses, fieldwork was again extremely time consuming and arduous. Respondents were traced all over Britain and abroad. One man was reinterviewed (by mail) in the Middle East, and another in Western Europe. Ultimately, 210 men, 70.0 per cent, were completely reinterviewed. Partial information was obtained about two men and a third had died. Twelve men, 4.0 per cent, refused to be reinterviewed and seventy-five, 25.0 per cent, could not be traced or contacted, even after extensive hunting (see *Table 12*). The final response rate was 94.6 per cent of contacts, but only 70.7 per cent of all those sought. The non-contact rate over the mean period of two-and-a-half years averaged 10.0 per cent per year, less than at one-year follow-up.

Current employment status

Altogether 107 alcohol producers and 103 control-group workers were reinterviewed completely. In addition, one man in each group was contacted but had sustained head injuries. Both were long-term hospital patients in consequence. Partial information was obtained

Table 12   Final response

Outcome	Alcohol producers	Controls	Total	
	N	N	N	%
Interviewed fully	107	103	210	70.0
Interviewed partially	1	1	2	0.7
Refused	7	5	12	4.0
Dead	1	—	1	0.3
Non-contacts	34	41	75	25.0
Total	150	150	300	100.0

from the wives of these two, who reported that both men had been injured in public house brawls.

As *Table 13* shows, sixty-two alcohol producers and seventy-nine controls were stables, still employed in the same subgroup as during 1975. Only five of the stable alcohol producers had changed their employment within the same trade, compared with forty-four of the controls. This is consistent with the fact that only a small minority of jobs in the Edinburgh area are connected with alcohol production. In most cases, a man changing his job would have to move outside the drink trade. Although only 212 of the original respondents were reinterviewed fully or partially two to three years later, contact was made with all of those men still working for their original (1975) employers. Of these only one man refused to be reinterviewed. The alcohol producers were significantly more likely than the controls to be with the same company as when interviewed originally, fifty-eight out of the 150, 38.7 per cent, compared with only thirty-five out of 150, 23.3 per cent.

Table 13   Current employment status

Status	Alcohol producers		Controls
With same company ⎱ in same	57		35
With different company ⎰ subgroup	5		44
Changed subgroup	38		8
Unemployed	8		17
Total	108		104

Reasons for changed employment

As *Table 13* shows, fifty-one alcohol producers and sixty-nine controls were no longer working for their original (1975) employers. Of these 120 men, six reported that they had been dismissed from their original employment. Four of these were formerly alcohol producers and two were control-group workers. Two of the four alcohol producers who reported having been dismissed stated that their dismissals had been due to being found drunk and incapable at work. In addition, eight of the forty-seven alcohol producers who left their original employment reported having done so for reasons associated with alcohol abuse. One of these eight men reported that he left his original brewery job because his workmates there were 'either drunkards or alcoholics and I got fed up with it all'. Seven men stated that they were becoming very concerned about their own heavy drinking and left in order to reduce it. Of these, two were drivers who reported that they were worried they would eventually lose their licences if caught driving under the influence of drink. One man stated that he was on the verge of being dismissed for persistent drunkenness at work. He left his original job in order to avoid having to admit to his next employers that he had been sacked. Another man who left in order to reduce his drinking stated that he had been persuaded to do so by his wife. Altogether ten of the fifty-one alcohol producers who had changed their original employment* and two of the sixty-nine controls who had done so stated that they had moved for some reason related to their own or to other people's drinking. Once more these results indicate clearly that a substantial minority of those leaving their jobs in the drink trade did so in order to reduce their levels of alcohol consumption in a 'drier' environment.

The stables

Sixty-two, 57.4 per cent, of the 108 alcohol producers and seventy-nine, 76.0 per cent, of the 104 controls who were reinterviewed were still engaged in the same type of work. The age distribution of the stables is shown in *Table 14*.

Consistent with differences noted in earlier interviews, the stable alcohol producers were more likely than the controls to be younger (see *Tables 5* and *8*). Age is once more taken into account in presenting the following results.

---

* Forty-six of these had left the drink trade.

Table 14 The stables : age

Age	Alcohol producers	Controls
Under 25	31	27
26 to 35	20	25
36 and above	11	27
Total	62	79

Drinking patterns

Abstainers and non-drinkers. Only two men, both of them control-group workers, reported that they never drank alcohol. One of these reported that he was an abstinent alcoholic. In addition three alcohol producers and eighteen controls had not drunk any alcohol during the week preceding interview. The numbers of non-drinking alcohol producers were too small to permit a statistical comparison, but the alcohol producers were clearly far less likely than the controls to be non-drinkers.

Drinking levels. There had been a considerable change in self-reported week's drinking habits since the initial interviews. The original alcohol consumption of the stables is shown in *Figure 9*.

Figure 9 THE "STABLES": INITIAL WEEK'S CONSUMPTION

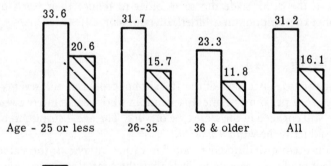

Age - 25 or less   26-35   36 & older   All

☐ Alcohol Producers
▨ Controls

Upon reinterview two to three years later there had been a general increase in week's alcohol consumption. This is shown in *Figure 10*.

Figure 10 THE "STABLES": WEEK'S CONSUMPTION TWO-THREE
YEARS LATER

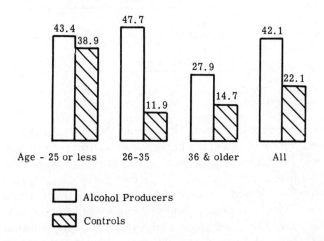

Percentage change. The overall increase in average alcohol consumption amongst the stable alcohol producers and controls was not significantly different, 34.9 per cent and 37.2 per cent respectively. Distinguishing the three different age groups, there were some interesting differences. Amongst those aged twenty-five or less, average consumption amongst the alcohol producers had increased by only 29.1 per cent compared with a strikingly high 88.3 per cent amongst the younger controls. In spite of this very great increase, the controls aged twenty-five or less had drunk on average only 38.9 units during the previous week, not significantly different from the 43.4 units consumed by the alcohol producers.

Alcohol producers aged between twenty-six and thirty-five had increased their average consumption from 31.7 units to 47.7 units, an increase of 50.5 per cent. In marked contrast, their counterparts in the control group had *decreased* their average consumption from 15.7 units to 11.9 units. Amongst those aged thirty-six and over there was no significant difference between the increased consumption of the alcohol producers and the controls, 19.7 per cent and 24.5 per cent respectively.

Change in units consumed.   The changes in average number of units consumed during the previous week are shown in *Table 15.*

Table 15   The stables: average change in units consumed

Age	Alcohol producers	Controls
25 or less	+ 9.8	+ 18.3
26 to 35	+ 16.0	— 3.8
36 and above	+ 4.6	+ 2.9
Total	+ 10.9	+ 6.0

+   indicates increase
—   indicates decrease

In spite of the age differences, these results show that the alcohol producers, who were as a group heavier drinkers than the controls, had maintained their higher alcohol consumption. By far the heaviest drinkers were both alcohol producers and controls aged twenty-five or less and the alcohol producers aged twenty-six to thirty-five. While the younger control-group workers had become nearly as heavy a drinking group as the young alcohol producers, the two subgroups retained very different consumption patterns amongst those aged twenty-six and above. One interpretation of these results is that, due to the natural history of relatively heavy drinking amongst young male manual workers, occupational differences were slight amongst younger men. It could be concluded that amongst older men employment in the drink trade serves to perpetuate the higher levels of alcohol consumption more commonly associated with youthfulness.

Heavy week's consumption.   Only three of the stables, all alcohol producers, reported having drunk 100 or more units (at least 50 pints of beer) during the week preceding interview. The average consumption of these men was 116.2 units. At their first interviews their average consumption was only 49.8 units.

Heaviest daily drinkers.   There was no difference between the numbers in either subgroup who had consumed large amounts of alcohol in a single day during the preceding week. Thirteen alcohol producers and eleven controls reported that on one day they had drunk at least 20 units (10 pints of beer). Of these, two alcohol producers and two controls stated that they had exceeded 30 units (15 pints of beer) in a single day during the preceding week. As at initial interview, the alcohol producers were not drinking significantly more in any one day than the controls. Their higher consumption was accounted for by the fact that they had drunk on more days during the previous week than the controls, 3.6 days on average compared with only 2.1 days.

Assessment of heavy drinking. Consistent with their greater level of alcohol consumption, the alcohol producers retained their significantly higher assessment of what constituted a heavy week's beer drinking. Their average evaluation was 60.0 pints compared with only 51.6 pints estimated by the controls. This 16.0 per cent difference was parallelled by a 21.4 per cent difference in estimates of the threshold of a heavy week's whisky drinking. The alcohol producers' average estimate was 3.4 bottles compared with only 2.8 bottles for the controls. It is notable that if one assumes a bottle of whisky contains 28 units (14 pints of beer), the alcohol producers' estimate of heavy beer drinking was in fact 26.0 per cent higher than that for whisky in terms of alcohol content. Similarly the controls estimated heavy beer consumption to be 31.5 per cent higher in alcohol content than heavy whisky drinking. This disparity is almost certainly attributable to the widespread misconception that whisky is much stronger in relation to beer than in fact it is. Several men stated that they were uncertain how much alcohol whisky contained but that a single glass of whisky (roughly equivalent to only half a pint of beer) contained as much as one or two pints of beer. One man, a brewing worker, actually stated that he did not know beer contained alcohol. When pressed to explain this, he reported that he believed its alcohol content to be so low as not to have any 'practical effects'. Several men stated that in their view anyone who drank spirits was a heavy drinker. Clearly the stereotype of the alcoholic as a person drinking spirits, if not meths, is still accepted by some people.

Drinking at work

The stable alcohol producers were significantly more likely than the stable control-group workers to report that they sometimes drank during working hours, thirty-nine out of sixty-two compared with only six out of seventy-nine. From their replies it was clear that the majority of alcohol producers had easy access to alcohol at work and were in practice free to drink it virtually unhindered in spite of company regulations which banned such drinking. Most of the thirty-nine alcohol producers who reported that they did sometimes drink at work made it clear that they did so on most working days and that this was fairly general behaviour. In contrast, the six control-group workers who reported drinking at work stressed that this was only an occasional practice. Some of the alcohol producers who denied drinking at work reported that they refrained from doing so for fear of 'losing control' of their drinking. Several stated that they were constrained from getting into the habit of drinking at work by the fact that they knew other workers who were conspicuously alcohol dependent, or who were somehow harmed by their drinking:

> 'A few of the boys I work with have let it [alcohol] get hold of them. Some are real alcoholics. They start to drink first thing in the morning. They are always asking me to drink with them, but I don't want to finish up like them. I never drink at work.'

> 'I used to drink but I hardly ever touch it at work now. I'm a driver and I can't afford to lose my licence. I have a wife and two kids and they are more important than a few drinks.'

> 'Some of the boys have been here too long. I know a couple who are "alkies". They can't do without a drink. It's just the job that does that.'

Perceptions of workmates' drinking habits

Consistent with their earlier interviews, the stable alcohol producers were significantly more likely than the stable controls to state that some of their workmates drank much more than they did, fifty-two out of sixty-two compared with fifty-three out of seventy-nine. The alcohol producers similarly were significantly more likely than the controls to report that some of those with whom they worked were heavy drinkers, fifty-one out of sixty-two compared with only fifty-four out of seventy-nine. Fifty alcohol producers and fifty-two of the controls estimated what percentage of their workmates were heavy drinkers. Once more the alcohol producers were significantly more likely to be willing to make such an assessment and those who did also produced a much higher estimate. The average judgement of the fifty alcohol producers was that 35.2 per cent of their workmates were heavy drinkers. The fifty-two controls estimated that only 26.9 per cent of their workmates were. Clearly the alcohol producers still were more likely to perceive their work environment as characterized by commonplace heavy drinking (even in terms of their more liberal definitions). Thirteen of the fifty alcohol producers making such an estimate reported that at least half of their workmates were heavy drinkers. Only seven of the fifty-two controls made similar statements. One brewery worker commented: 'The blokes here are more interested in drink than they are in women.'

Perceived harm

In spite of the alcohol producers' greater likelihood of perceiving their workmates as heavy drinkers, they were not significantly more likely to report that their workmates suffered due to drinking. Thirty of the sixty-two stable alcohol producers and thirty-six of the seventy-nine stable controls gave this reply.

There was a striking difference in the types of alcohol-related harm that the two subgroups reported. As during the earlier interviews, the alcohol producers were significantly more likely than the controls to state that at least one of those with whom they worked was an 'alcoholic'. When specifying what types of alcohol-related damage they noticed at work, this was the most common reply, given by fourteen of the thirty-one alcohol producers who gave a specific answer. Only six of the thirty-seven controls giving a specific answer referred to alcoholics. In contrast, the most common types of harm reported by the controls (twenty) related to inefficiency at work caused by drunkenness and hangovers. Only twelve of the alcohol producers referred to this. It is clear that the alcohol producers as a group were more likely to perceive their workmates as regular heavy drinkers, of whom some had long-term, serious alcohol problems. The controls were less likely to share these perceptions, and more likely to report more sporadic problems due to occasional binges. Many of the alcohol producers supported their reports of alcoholic workmates by describing these men having to drink upon arrival at work to allay withdrawal symptoms. It was clear that some of these individuals were quite conspicuously alcohol dependent. There was no difference between the proportion of alcohol producers and controls reporting specific types of alcohol-related harm amongst their workmates. Even so, the difference between the types of harm described are very important and are consistent with the heavier drinking evident in the brewing and distilling firms.

Alcohol-related problems

Both subgroups had increased their alcohol consumption considerably over two to three years. Only the alcohol producers had also increased their overall score of problems experienced from the list of eighteen (see *Appendix Ib*, question 13). They had significantly increased their average score from 3.0 to 3.7. The reasons for this disparity are indicated in *Table 16*.

Table 16   The stables: changes in problem scores

Problem score	Alcohol producers	Controls
Increase	33	29
Decrease	15	23
Same	14	27
Total	62	79

At the first reinterview there had been no difference between the changed problem scores of the two subgroups (see *Table 10*). At least one year later the higher alcohol consumption of the alcohol producers had led to thirty-three of the sixty-two stables reporting an increase in the number of the alcohol-related problems they had experienced. It could be that many of the problems from the list, such as being criticized for one's drinking, only begin to occur once a regular pattern of heavy drinking has been established for some time. This may explain why the one-year follow-up failed to detect any difference between the two stable subgroups, even though both had increased their alcohol consumption.

Physical damage

Four alcohol producers and eleven controls reported that they had suffered from either a stomach ulcer or liver trouble since their initial interviews. The number of alcohol producers with new physical damage is too small to permit a statistical comparison. Even so, the larger proportion of control-group workers with new physical damage is explained by the fact that they were generally older than the alcohol producers. Only one of the alcohol producers and four of the controls aged twenty-five or less had new physical damage. There was no significant difference between the average ages of those in either subgroup with new physical damage: the average of the four alcohol producers was 31.5 years compared with 32.7 years for the eleven controls. Apart from one man in each subgroup who had contracted TB since initial interview, all of the newly acquired physical damage related to stomach ulcers. Only four of those with new physical damage, all controls, had stopped drinking. Five men, two alcohol producers and three controls, reported that their previous week's consumption had exceeded 40 units (20 pints). The average consumption of the four alcohol producers and seven controls who were still drinking was 41.6 units, surprising in view of the fact that all reported having been urged to drink less by their doctors. The overall prevalence of alcohol-related physical damage was as follows:

Gastritis: As at one year follow-up, this was the most common of the four disabilities. Once more there was no significant difference between the proportion of alcohol producers and controls reporting that they had suffered from this complaint, eleven and seventeen respectively.

Stomach ulcers were reported by six alcohol producers and twelve control-group workers. Again there was no significant difference in this respect between the two subgroups.

Liver cirrhosis or some type of 'liver trouble' was reported by one alcohol producer and three controls.

TB of the chest was reported by three alcohol producers and two controls.

Altogether, sixteen of the sixty-two stable alcohol producers (25.8 per cent) and twenty-five of the seventy-nine stable controls (31.6 per cent) reported having suffered from one or more of the physical conditions. There was no significant difference between the two subgroups in spite of the heavier patterns of alcohol consumption amongst the alcohol producers.

Alcohol-related convictions

Twenty-three individuals, twelve alcohol producers and eleven controls, reported having been convicted of at least one alcohol-related offence since their original interview. The alcohol producers, in spite of their higher level of drinking, were not significantly more likely than the controls to report such a conviction during the study period. As at the earlier interviews, most of these offences involved either breach of the peace (sixteen), drunken driving (six), drunk and disorderly (five), or other illegal acts attributed by the respondents to their drinking.

Separation/divorce

Seven men, one alcohol producer and six control-group workers, reported that they had either become separated from their wives, or had been divorced, since their original interviews. The alcohol producer, a man of twenty-five at initial interview, was quite a heavy drinker. His previous week's consumption was 89.5 units (around 45 pints of beer). He attributed his divorce 'partly' to his drinking. The six control-group workers were not heavy drinkers, having an average previous week's consumption of only 13.2 units (6½ pints of beer). Their average age upon initial interview was 40.8 years.

Absenteeism

There was no significant difference between the general absenteeism of the two subgroups. Fourteen alcohol producers and twenty-one controls reported that they had taken at least one day off work during the past four weeks. Of these, four alcohol producers and three controls stated that they had been absent from work on at least one day due to some alcohol-related cause. All seven men reported that their absences had been due to oversleeping or feeling ill after a 'heavy night's drinking'.

Admission of alcohol-related problems

There was no significant difference between the proportion of alcohol producers and controls who reported that there had been a time when drinking had caused them problems. Eleven alcohol producers and fourteen controls stated that they had experienced some kind of alcohol-related problem. Of these only five of the alcohol producers and eight of the controls stated that they were currently experiencing such problems. All except three of these twelve men were aged twenty-five or less at their first interview. The average previous week's alcohol consumption of these thirteen men was 57.1 units, well above the average, which for alcohol producers was 42.1 units and for controls was 22.1 units (see *Figure 10*). Their average problem score out of the list of eighteen was also significantly above average, 6.6. Each of these (mainly young) men explained that they were getting into quite serious trouble due to excessive drinking. They mentioned financial, marital, occupational, and physical difficulties. One man stated that he was an alcoholic, and had for some time been a conscientious member of Alcoholics Anonymous. He reported that since his original interview he had lost his job and his wife had left him due to his drinking. Now successfully abstinent, he had returned to work in the drink trade. Only one other man reported having tried, unsuccessfully, to stop drinking. The others appeared torn between giving way to the pressures to drink and the realization that they were suffering as a consequence of drinking.

Parasuicide (attempted suicide) and psychiatric illness

None of the stables had made a parasuicidal act since interview. Even so, six alcohol producers and seventeen controls reported that they had experienced 'trouble with their nerves' since their initial interviews. There was no significant difference in the proportions in either subgroup giving this reply. Seven men, four alcohol producers and three controls, volunteered that their depression/stress had been linked with their drinking. The average previous week's alcohol consumption of the six alcohol producers was significantly above average for their stable subgroup, 52.9 units compared with only 40.9 units. The average previous week's alcohol consumption of the seventeen controls was, however, not different from other stable controls, being only 22.2 units. While the alcohol producers were no more likely than the controls to have experienced recent 'trouble with their nerves', those who had were distinctly heavy drinkers, while the controls were not. It could be that, working in an environment where alcohol was accessible, they had responded to stress by drinking. The numbers of those linking their mental distress to alcohol are too small to justify any firm conclusions to this effect.

These results show that the general conclusions of the one-year follow-up were confirmed. Remaining in the drink trade had clearly led to greatly increased alcohol consumption and to an increase in alcohol-related problem scores. In view of this it is perhaps surprising that the stable alcohol producers were not significantly more likely to have experienced new physical damage or alcohol-related convictions.

The leavers

Forty-six men had left the drink trade since their initial interviews. Thirty-eight of these were working in control-group occupations with a low alcoholism rate. Eight were currently unemployed. As in Chapter 6 these two groups will be described separately in order to distinguish the effects of leaving the drink trade from the effects of leaving work altogether.

Table 17   The leavers : age

Age	Working	Unemployed	Total
25 or less	18	6	24
26 to 35	11	1	12
36 and older	9	1	10
Total	38	8	46

As at the one-year follow-up, most of the leavers were young. As *Table 17* shows, twenty-four, 52.2 per cent, were aged twenty-five or less, and only ten, 21.7 per cent, were aged thirty-six or over. In fact the age distribution of the leavers was not significantly different from that of the sixty-two stable alcohol producers who were also reinterviewed two to three years later (see *Table 14*).

Drinking patterns

Abstainers and non-drinkers.   None of the leavers reported that they had not drunk any alcohol during the previous week.

Drinking levels. In confirmation of the results of the one-year follow-up (*Figures 6, 7*, and *8*), there had again been a decline in the previous week's alcohol consumption of the forty-six leavers. This is shown in *Figure 11.*

Figure 11 THE "LEAVERS": CONSUMPTION CHANGES OVER TWO-THREE YEARS

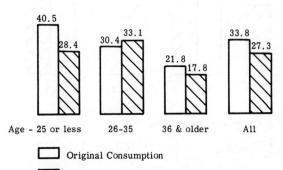

Age - 25 or less   26-35   36 & older   All

☐ Original Consumption

▨ Consumption Two - Three Years Later

In fact this decrease in consumption was only significant amongst the twenty-four leavers aged twenty-five or less. There had been no significant change amongst the older men. Those aged twenty-six to thirty-five had slightly, but not significantly, increased their consumption.

Once more, there was a difference between those leavers who were still working and those who were currently unemployed. Those still working, but now in control-group type employment, had decreased their average previous week's consumption by 30.9 per cent. In marked contrast, those who were unemployed had slightly, but not significantly, *increased* their average consumption by 4.4 per cent. This slight change was also in contrast to the trend in consumption noted amongst the unemployed leavers reinterviewed one year after initial interview. They had decreased their original consumption by 40.1 per cent (see *Figure 8*). Unemployment clearly had a very different effect upon drinking habits from entry into a 'low-risk' control-group type of job. These differences are shown in *Figures 12* and *13*.

The changes shown in *Figure 13* need to be assessed with caution since only eight leavers are represented therein, six of whom were aged twenty-five or less. While the number of unemployed leavers

Figure 12 THE "LEAVERS": THOSE STILL WORKING (N38)

CONSUMPTION CHANGES OVER TWO - THREE YEARS

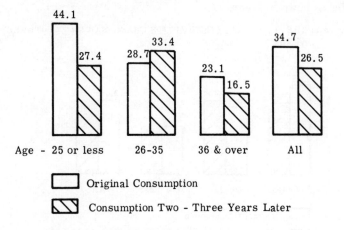

Figure 13 THE "LEAVERS": THE UNEMPLOYED (N8)

CONSUMPTION CHANGES OVER TWO - THREE YEARS

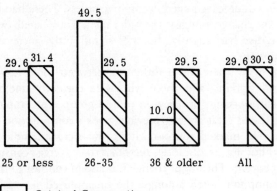

is too small to enable a statistical comparison, it is of interest that while leaving the drink trade to work elsewhere had led to a significant fall in alcohol consumption, leaving the drink trade to become unemployed did not. This could be interpreted as indicating that the stress or boredom of unemployment is as likely to lead to heavy drinking as the availability and peer pressure to drink within alcohol production. A further insight into the relative influences upon drinking patterns of alcohol production, control-group employment, and unemployment is provided by the seventeen control-group workers who were unemployed when reinterviewed two to three years later. Whereas the seventy-nine stable controls had increased their consumption by 37.2 per cent over this period, those who had become unemployed had increased theirs by significantly more, 54.5 per cent. This is consistent with the trend noted at one-year follow-up and reported in Chapter 6. The consumption changes of the seventeen unemployed control-group workers are shown in *Figure 14*.

Figure 14 THE UNEMPLOYED CONTROLS (N17)

CONSUMPTION CHANGES OVER TWO - THREE YEARS

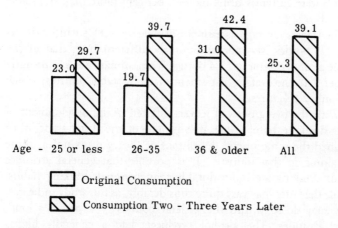

Age - 25 or less   26-35   36 & older   All

☐ Original Consumption

▨ Consumption Two - Three Years Later

Heavy week's consumption. Four of the leavers reported having drunk 100 or more units (at least 50 pints of beer) during the week preceding interview. Two of these men were currently working in control-group type jobs, two were unemployed. The average week's consumption of these four men was 128 units (64 pints). At their initial interviews their average consumption had been only 54.5 units (26.5 pints).

These numbers are too small to permit statistical comparisons.

Even so, these four comprised 8.7 per cent of the leavers. Only three of the 141 stables, 2.1 per cent, had become such heavy drinkers.

Assessment of heavy drinking

Twenty-one of the forty-six leavers had increased their assessment of what amount constituted a heavy week's beer drinking. Eighteen had decreased their assessment. The leavers' average assessment of the threshold of heavy beer drinking was 58.2 pints, not significantly different from the 60.0 pints which was the average estimate of the stable alcohol producers. There was no difference between the average assessment of those leavers who were still working and those who were unemployed. While the leavers' estimate of heavy beer drinking did not differ significantly from the stable alcohol producers, it was significantly higher than the 51.6 pints which was the average estimate of the stable control-group workers. This difference of assessment was broadly consistent with the fact that the leavers were currently drinking 23.5 per cent more than the stable controls.

The leavers' average assessment of a heavy week's whisky drinking, 3.5 bottles, was not significantly different from that of the stable alcohol producers, 3.4 bottles. This estimate was significantly higher than the average assessment made by stable controls, which was only 2.8 bottles.

While the two groups of leavers differed in the development of their drinking habits since moving out of the drink trade, they retained the same liberal definitions of 'heavy drinking' as those remaining in that industry. It is possible that general attitudes about drinking are more durable than personal drinking habits. While the latter may vary quite considerably, as this study indicates, they may do so within the general bounds of a person's long-term attitudes. The alcohol producers had a generally higher assessment of heavy drinking at initial interview. Possibly they had such an assessment before entering the trade, since they appear to have retained it even after leaving and reducing their general level of consumption.

Drinking at work

In marked contrast with the 'stable' alcohol producers, only four of the thirty-eight working 'leavers' reported that they sometimes drank at work. All four made it clear that they only did so occasionally.

Perceptions of workmates' drinking habits

Consistent with their reduced level of alcohol consumption, the thirty-eight leavers who were working were significantly less likely than the sixty-two stable alcohol producers to state that they worked with men who drank much more than they did, only twenty-five out of thirty-eight compared with fifty-two out of sixty-two. Similarly, the working leavers were also significantly less likely than the stable alcohol producers to report that they worked with heavy drinkers, only twenty-four out of thirty-eight compared with fifty-one out of sixty-two. The average estimate of the twenty-four men who reported working with heavy drinkers was that 24.7 per cent of their workmates were in this category. This estimate was significantly lower than that of the stable alcohol producers, 35.2 per cent, and was very close to that of the stable controls, 26.9 per cent.

Perceived harm

Seventeen of the thirty-eight working leavers reported that some of those with whom they worked in their new control-group type jobs suffered through drinking. This proportion was not significantly different either from that amongst the stable alcohol producers or the stable controls. Of the fifteen leavers who specified the type of harm they noticed, eleven referred to drunkenness or inefficiency at work. Two men reported that they worked alongside alcoholics and two reported that workmates experienced marital problems caused by excessive drinking. This pattern of response was more like that of the stable controls than that of the stable alcohol producers.

Alcohol-related problems

Thirty-two of the forty-six leavers reported that they had experienced more of the list of eighteen problems than they had mentioned when interviewed originally (see *Appendix 1b*, question 13). The trends in problems are shown in *Table 18*.

As indicated in *Table 18*, twenty-five of the thirty-eight leavers who were currently working, and seven of the eight who were unemployed, had increased their problem scores. Amongst both groups of leavers there had been a significant increase in problem scores. The average score of the thirty-eight leavers who were working had risen from 2.2 to 3.8. That of the eight unemployed leavers had risen from 2.7 to 4.7. The current average problem score of all forty-six leavers was 4.0. This was not significantly higher than the current average score of the sixty-two stable alcohol producers, which was 3.7.

Table 18   The leavers : changes in problem scores

Problem score	Those still working (N38)	Those unemployed (N 8)
Increase	25	7
Decrease	7	1
Same	6	0
Total	38	8

The chronology of these newly encountered problems is not clear. Some men reported that they had experienced alcohol-related problems while still working in the drink trade. Others stated that they had encountered them since leaving. It cannot, therefore, be inferred that this increase over two to three years in alcohol-related problems necessarily indicated an increase in current problems. In fact, the general decline in the average week's alcohol consumption of the leavers would be more consistent with a decline in current problems.

Physical damage

Two of the forty-six leavers reported that they had developed stomach ulcers since their initial interviews. Both men were in their early thirties and were currently working in control-group type jobs. One was not a heavy drinker, and had not been such at initial interview. He stated that his ulcer was unrelated to drinking. The second man's previous week's alcohol consumption had been 130 units, equivalent to 65 pints of beer. He conceded that his ulcer was probably influenced, if not wholly caused, by his drinking. Apart from these two men, both of whom had also suffered from gastritis, a further ten of the forty-six leavers reported that they had suffered from gastritis. The gastritis rate amongst the leavers was not significantly higher than that amongst the stable alcohol producers or controls.

Alcohol-related convictions

Ten of the forty-six leavers, 21.7 per cent, reported that they had been convicted of at least one alcohol-related offence since their original interviews two to three years earlier. The proportion of those with such recent convictions was not significantly different from that amongst the stables, either alcohol producers or controls. Between them the ten leavers reported having gained a total of at least forty drink-related offences during the study period. Eight of the ten had been convicted of breach of the peace between one and thirteen times. Of these, two had also been convicted of assaults which they ascribed to their drinking. Both men had served prison sentences for these assaults. One of the eight had also been convicted of theft which he attributed to drinking. A ninth man had been convicted of drunken driving and the tenth had been convicted three times of thefts which he stated were precipitated by the fact that he was drunk at the time. All of these offenders were young, aged thirty-two or less, and two were unemployed. Not surprisingly the average previous week's alcohol consumption of these ten men was significantly higher than that of all of the other leavers, 43.6 units compared with only 22.8 units. Even so, the average 'problem score' of these men did not differ from that of the other leavers.

Separation/divorce

Four of the leavers reported that they had become separated from their wives or had been divorced since their original interviews. One of these men stated that his drinking had contributed to his marital problems. A second man, currently unemployed and drinking heavily (50 pints during the previous week), reported that he had turned to drink because his marriage had broken up. In spite of this he stated that he was currently drinking less than when his wife had originally left him several months earlier. This man frankly conceded that he was using drink as a form of self-medication:

'Sometimes I just want to get steaming [drunk] and to forget everything.'

Admission of alcohol-related problems

Nine of the forty-six leavers reported that, at some time in their lives, they had experienced alcohol-related problems. Six of those men were currently engaged in control-group type jobs. Two were unemployed. Only two of these eight men stated that they were currently experiencing difficulties with their drinking. Both men were working and both were young (eighteen and thirty-two). Neither appeared to be exceptionally heavy drinkers, having consumed 24 units (12 pints of beer) and 52 units (26 pints of beer) respectively during the week preceding interview. Both men reported getting into fights with people while drunk and reported that they frequently became drunk at weekends. The older man, who was married, reported experiencing serious arguments with his wife due to his drunkenness at weekends.

As indicated by the one-year follow-up, those who had left the drink trade and moved into control-group type jobs had significantly reduced their drinking levels. Presumably this was due to the reduced availability of alcohol, combined with less encouragement to drink, in their new work situations. Those who had left the drink trade and who had become unemployed had not reduced their alcohol consumption. This could indicate that unemployment is, like employment in the drink trade, a 'high-risk' status. This possibility was further supported by the 54.5 per cent increase in alcohol consumption by the seventeen control-group workers who had become unemployed. In spite of the fall in alcohol consumption amongst the employed leavers, their assessments of what constituted heavy drinking remained unchanged. The changes evident amongst those leaving alcohol production for control-group type jobs were in marked contrast to those whose job changes had been in the opposite direction.

The entrants

Eight men who were control-group workers when first interviewed in 1975 had entered the drink trade (six) or another 'high-risk' occupation, the Merchant Navy (two). Their ages are shown in *Table 19*.

Table 19 The entrants : age

Age	Number
25 or less	2
26 to 35	4
36 and older	2
Total	8

Drinking patterns

Abstainers and non-drinkers. One of the entrants reported that he had not drunk any alcohol during the week preceding the interview. He stated that he had liver cirrhosis and was an abstinent alcoholic.

Drinking levels. Consistent with the experience of the two entrants interviewed at one-year follow-up, entering the drink trade or other 'high-risk' jobs had been accompanied by a dramatic increase in alcohol consumption. This is shown in *Figure 15* (overleaf).

As *Figure 15* shows, the average previous week's alcohol consumption of the eight entrants had risen from 17.3 units (around 8½ pints of beer) to 48.5 units (about 24 pints) over the study period. This constitutes an increase of 280.0 per cent. In fact, only the two entrants who were aged thirty-six and over had not significantly increased their alcohol consumption. The other six younger entrants had increased their average weekly consumption from 14.3 units (about 7 pints of beer) to 45.3 units (about 22½ pints), an increase of 316.8 per cent. This increase is in complete contrast to the 30.9 per cent *decrease* in consumption noted amongst the thirty-eight men who had left the drink trade to work in control-group type jobs (see *Figure 12*).

Heavy week's consumption. Two of the eight entrants reported having drunk more than 100 units (50 pints of beer) during the week preceding interview.

These results apply only to eight men. Even so, they are extremely clear-cut and indicate that, while leaving the drink trade

114 *Drinking Careers*

Figure 15 THE "ENTRANTS" (N8) CONSUMPTION CHANGES OVER

TWO - THREE YEARS

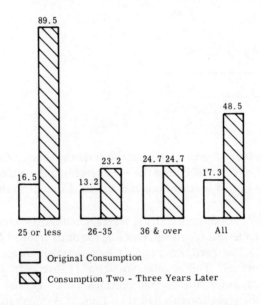

Original Consumption

Consumption Two - Three Years Later

was generally followed by a significant fall in alcohol consumption, joining a 'high-risk' industry had an (at least) equally significant impact on alcohol consumption.

Assessment of heavy drinking

The average assessment of the eight entrants was that to be a heavy drinker a man would have to drink either 57 pints of beer or 2.1 bottles of whisky in a single week. These estimates were significantly lower than those of the stable alcohol producers yet not significantly different from those of the stable controls. This is surprising since the entrants were currently drinking more than twice as much, on average, as the stable controls, and were even drinking more, though not significantly so, than the stable alcohol producers (see *Figure 10*). Once more, the changes in drinking habits of a subgroup of workers had not been reflected by changes in their assessments of what constituted 'heavy' drinking. Even so, it must be noted that the average consumption of the eight entrants was still below what they considered to be the threshold of 'heavy' drinking.

Drinking at work

Five of the eight entrants now reported that they sometimes drank at work. While these numbers are too small to justify statistical comparisons, it is clear that these men were conforming to the common practice amongst the alcohol producers. None of the entrants had reported drinking at work when originally interviewed in 1975.

Perception of workmates' drinking habits

Also broadly consistent with the stable alcohol producers, six of the eight entrants reported that some of those with whom they now worked drank much more than they did. In addition the same six men stated that some of their workmates were heavy drinkers. Their average estimate was that 60.5 per cent of those with whom they now worked were heavy drinkers. This estimate was significantly higher than that of either the stable alcohol producers or the stable controls, which were 35.2 per cent and 26.9 per cent respectively. It was also significantly higher than that of the thirty-eight leavers currently working in control-group type jobs which was only 24.7 per cent.

Perceived harm

Five of the eight entrants reported that some of their workmates suffered due to their drinking. Two of these reported working with alcoholics and three reported seeing fellow employees who were drunk or inefficient at work due to excessive drinking.

Alcohol-related problems

The average problem score of the eight entrants was 8.4, significantly higher than those of either the stables or the leavers. Four of the eight entrants reported having experienced more than ten of the eighteen problems related to their drinking (see *Appendix Ib*, question 13). One of these four reported that he no longer drank alcohol, and was trying to abstain. The average previous week's consumption of the other three was still high, 82.7 units (about 41 pints of beer). One of the three had reportedly drunk 84 pints during the week preceding his reinterview.

Physical damage

Two of the eight entrants reported that they had, at some time, suffered from gastritis. One of these also reported that since his original interview in 1975 he had developed liver cirrhosis. He was the individual referred to in the previous paragraph who had been abstinent for some time on his doctor's orders. A third entrant had developed a stomach ulcer over the study period. All three men reported that these physical disabilities were due to their drinking. While these numbers are too small to warrant statistical comparisons, it is notable that three of the eight entrants, 37.5 per cent, had some form of physical damage which they frankly attributed to their recent or current level of drinking.

Alcohol-related convictions

Two of the eight entrants reported having been convicted of alcohol-related offences during the study period. One of these had been convicted of breach of the peace, the second for drunken driving.

Separation/divorce

None of the entrants were newly separated or divorced.

Absenteeism

Three of the eight entrants reported having missed at least one day's work during the previous month. None of these three stated that their absences were in any way related to drinking.

Admission of alcohol-related problems

Five of the eight entrants reported that, at some time in their lives, drinking had caused them problems. Three of these men stated that they were currently experiencing problems with their drinking. Two of these three stated that in their view they were 'alcoholics'. When asked to explain what they meant, both provided lengthy statements to the effect that they were 'addicted' to alcohol, physically dependent, and drinking continuously in order to ward off withdrawal symptoms. One man reported that he had once experienced delirium tremens, although this had been before the study period. Both had clearly been suffering a great many difficulties due to their drinking. One of these two men was the merchant seaman whose greatly increased alcohol consumption and newly acquired alcohol-related problems were described in the previous chapter. The other man was currently working in a brewery. Neither of these men conceded that they had been attracted into 'high-risk' jobs because of their predilection to drink heavily, although all three conceded that their drinking habits had been exacerbated by the considerable pressures to drink which they now encountered at work. All of these men were advised how to contact local alcoholism treatment agencies.

Parasuicide (attempted suicide) and psychiatric illness

One of the eight entrants, a twenty-four-year-old brewery worker, reported having taken a deliberate overdose during the study period. He attributed this event, not to his drinking (which was light), but to a broken love affair. He and two of the other entrants reported that they had recently had 'trouble with their nerves' and had consulted their general practitioners about this. The other two men were those reporting that they were alcoholics.

It is of considerable interest why the entrants were so much more extreme in their changed drinking habits and other differences from the controls than those newly recruited to the drink trade who were interviewed in 1975. Two reasons may explain this: first, the entrants had been in the drink trade or in other high-risk jobs for much longer than the new recruits to alcohol production during 1975. They had therefore had more time to be influenced by their job milieu. Second, it is possible that those respondents who were willing to be reinterviewed were especially well-disposed to, or interested in, the study. Certainly some individuals who were less enthusiastic were excluded since they refused to be re-interviewed.

As indicated by the one-year follow-up, remaining in, leaving, or entering the drink trade or other high-risk jobs had been accompanied by some dramatic changes in drinking habits. Before discussing these further, it is of interest to examine how, overall, the original alcohol producers and controls had changed their levels of alcohol consumption during the study period.

Overall changes in alcohol consumption

Altogether, 107 alcohol producers and 103 control-group workers were fully reinterviewed between two and three years after their original 1975 interviews. The changes in average previous week's alcohol consumption of these respondents is shown in *Table 20*.

Table 20   Changes in average week's alcohol consumption during the study period

Consumption	Alcohol producers	Controls
Original consumption (units)	32.3	17.7
Current consumption (units)	35.8	26.9
Percentage increase	10.8%	51.9%
Increase in units	3.5	9.2

As this table indicates, the 107 alcohol producers had maintained their higher average weekly level of consumption. Even so, the 103 control-group workers had increased their average consumption by much more than the alcohol producers, 51.9 per cent compared with only 10.8 per cent. The average alcohol producer had increased his consumption by only 3.5 units (less than two pints of beer) whereas the average control-group worker had increased his consumption level by 9.2 units (just over 4½ pints). The greater increase in consumption amongst the control-group workers was due to the fact that forty-six of the 107 alcohol producers had left the drink trade and had reduced their average consumption, whereas twenty-five of the controls had either entered high-risk occupations or had become unemployed and increased their average consumption. The fact that the control group had greatly closed the gap between their consumption and that of the alcohol producers was entirely due to job change, together with the age differences existing between the two subgroups.

There had not been any significant shifts in the percentages of respondents in either subgroup who were non-drinkers, medium, or heavy drinkers. This is shown in *Table 21*. For the purposes of this table, previous week's alcohol consumption is divided into four categories as follows.

(a) non-drinkers: no alcohol consumed during week preceding interview
(b) light drinkers: those who had consumed 1 to 39 units
(c) drinkers: those who had consumed 40 to 99 units
(d) heavy drinkers: those who had consumed 100 or more units.

Table 21 Overall change in drinking status during the study period

Drinking status	Alcohol producers (N107)		Controls (N103)	
	Original %	Current %	Original %	Current %
Non-drinkers	4.7	2.8	17.5	18.5
Light drinkers	66.4	66.4	69'9	62.1
Drinkers	26.1	24.3	12.6	17.5
Heavy drinkers	2.8	6.5	—	1.9
Total	100.0	100.0	100.0	100.0

As *Table 21* shows there had been a slight, but not statistically significant, shift in the patterns of alcohol consumption in the two subgroups, notably a small increase in the percentage of those in either subgroup who had consumed at least 100 units (50 pints of beer) during the week preceding interview.

As *Tables 20* and *21* indicate, there had been a general rise in the alcohol consumption of both subgroups. Presumably this was in part a reflection of the fact that over two to three years the population as a whole was drinking more. The main changes in alcohol consumption, as indicated earlier in this chapter, were associated with *current* job status ('stable', 'leaver', 'entrant', or unemployed) rather than to which subgroup each respondent had belonged in 1975.

The heavy drinkers and alcoholics

By the end of the study period nine respondents reported that their previous week's alcohol consumption had been at least 100 units (50 pints of beer). Two of these men, plus a third who was currently abstinent, reported that, in their view, they were now alcoholics.

Seven of these ten men were alcohol producers and three were control-group workers at their initial interviews in 1975. By the end of the study period only one remained in control-group type of employment. Two were unemployed, two had entered 'high-risk' jobs from the control group and one had changed from alcohol production to another 'high-risk' job, fishing. Apart from the abstinent alcoholic (an Alcoholics Anonymous member), who was forty-seven at initial interview, all of the other nine men were relatively young, aged between twenty-three and thirty-three at their initial interviews.

It is of great practical relevance whether the initial interviews with these men provided 'clues' that they would, by the end of the study period, be drinking so heavily or would, by their own admission, be alcoholics.

While these ten men are too few to justify statistical comparison with the other respondents, they were in fact different from the rest in some respects. At their original interviews eight of the ten reported that they had previously worked in 'high-risk' jobs, such as the Merchant Navy, armed forces, or as bar staff. This is very different from the proportion of other respondents with such job histories, only ninety-six out of 290, 33.1 per cent. The remaining two men had reported poor work records, having had more than five jobs in the previous two years. All ten were therefore atypical in relation to their previous employment. The family backgrounds of these ten men were not atypical, although one man reported that his father had been an alcoholic and a second stated that both of his parents were heavy drinkers. No other biographical characteristics distinguished these men from the rest of the study group. Even so, their average previous week's alcohol consumption in 1975, 63.1 units, was significantly higher than that of the other 290 respondents, 26.0 units. Consistent with this, their average problem score, 5.3, was also significantly higher than that of the other respondents, 3.1.

It is of interest whether these men who became heavy drinkers or alcoholics (or both) could have been identified as likely to do so at the outset of this study. Clearly their previous job histories were atypical, and so were their existing levels of drinking and alcohol-related problems. It remains doubtful whether job applicants would give honest replies about their drinking habits or alcohol-related problems to a prospective employer, especially if they thought such factors would affect their chances of getting a job. If employers can take any guidance from these findings, it is probable that previous work history is the most useful guide, about which honest information is more likely to be obtained than about drinking habits.

Getting married

The preceding results show fairly clearly that most of the changes noted at one-year follow-up had been consolidated and confirmed. Major changes in drinking behaviour had ensued in association with changes in job situation. Another important change in life situation that had befallen some of those originally interviewed in 1975 was that some had subsequently married. It has been noted elsewhere that most heavy drinkers are young, single males (Dight 1976). In addition it has been reported that marriage may be a potent reason for reducing one's drinking (Cahalan and Room 1972). The effects of marriage on the study group are described below.

Eleven of the 210 respondents who were reinterviewed completely two to three years after their original interviews had married during the study period. Eight of these men were alcohol producers, three were control-group workers. All were young, their average age being only 22.2 years. In marked contrast to the other 199 men reinterviewed during 1977 or. 1978, the average previous week's alcohol consumption of those who were newly married had *decreased* by 13.2 per cent. The average consumption of all other respondents had increased by 26.7 per cent. None of the eleven newly married men were heavy drinkers. Over the study period their average consumption had decreased from 31.8 units to 27.4 units. The numbers of newly married men within each subcategory of alcohol producers and controls (e.g. 'stables', 'leavers', 'entrants') were too small to justify statistical comparisons. Even so, they had not, as a group, followed the general trend of increased consumption in spite of the fact that they were still all young men. These results only applied to eleven men. In view of these extremely small numbers, it is not possible to draw any firm conclusions about the relationship between marriage and alcohol consumption. Even though the *average* consumption of these eleven men had decreased, the *individual* consumption of seven had actually increased. In any event the reasons for the overall decrease in alcohol consumption cannot be attributed to marriage. There may have been other reasons. This topic could usefully be examined further.

Previous employment in alcohol-related jobs

As noted in Chapter 5, a third of the men interviewed during 1975 reported having been previously employed in 'high-risk' jobs, such as in the armed forces, Merchant Navy, or the drink trade. At their initial interview these men were not drinking more, and did not have higher rates of alcohol-related problems, than their counterparts who did not have previous experience of 'high-risk' jobs.

It is of interest to note that even at the final interview two to three years later men with previous 'high-risk' jobs were still no different from other respondents in relation to drinking habits, alcohol-related problems, or job status. This is important, since it was possible that a subgroup of men might have been identified who were habitually heavy drinkers and who preferred 'high-risk' jobs. In fact this study did not produce evidence for such clear-cut preferences. These findings lend further support to the importance of *current* occupation in influencing current drinking habits.

Non-response

All except two of those who were still in their original (1975) jobs were successfully reinterviewed two to three years later. One of the alcohol producers had died and a second refused to be reinterviewed. A total of eighty-eight of the original 300 respondents, 29.3 per cent, were not reinterviewed for various reasons: apart from the single death, twelve men refused to be reinterviewed, and seventy-five could not be contacted.

The death.   One of the alcohol producers, who had been twenty-one when interviewed in 1975, had been killed in a traffic accident in 1977. There was no evidence linking his tragic death with his drinking. Also, he had been a light drinker with no alcohol-related problems when interviewed two years before his death.

The refusals. Seven alcohol producers and five of the control group refused to be reinterviewed. All except one alcohol producer had left their original employment. As remarked in Chapter 6, it is possible that such men were influenced to refuse because the follow-up interview involved giving up some of their leisure time, whereas the original interview had been in their employers' time. Four of the refusals were openly hostile when asked to be reinterviewed. In addition, the one man still in his original employment as a brewery worker was very upset. When the nature and purpose of the reinterview was explained to him he became tearful and stated that he did not want to discuss his drinking which was clearly a delicate subject.

Eleven of the twelve refusals were young, aged thirty-five or under. None of the five control-group workers had reported high alcohol consumptions during their 1975 interviews. Even so, two of the seven alcohol producers had reported quite high weekly consumptions, 60 units (30 pints of beer) and 61 units (30½ pints) respectively. In addition, one alcohol producer and one control-group worker both reported having experienced eleven of the eighteen alcohol-related problems (see *Appendix Ia*, question 36). Apart from the youthfulness and evident mobility of these twelve men, there was no evidence from their 1975 interviews that they differed from the rest of the study group.

The non-contacts. Seventy-five respondents, thirty-four alcohol producers and forty-one control-group workers, could not be traced for reinterview, even after extensive inquiries. All had left both their original (1975) employment and their original addresses.

There was no significant difference between the proportion in either subgroup who could not be contacted for reinterview.

Both amongst the alcohol producers and the controls, those who were not contacted for reinterview were significantly more likely to be young than were those in each subgroup who were reinterviewed. Altogether, forty-three of the seventy-five non-contacts were aged twenty-five or less compared with only seventy-six of the 212 men who were reinterviewed fully or partially two to three years after initial interview.

Neither the alcohol producers nor the controls who were non-contacts differed from their counterparts who were reinterviewed in their initial alcohol consumption or the number of alcohol-related problems that they reported having experienced. In addition, the non-contacts did not significantly differ from those who were reinterviewed in relation to biographical characteristics, and all of the other alcohol-related problems (e.g. physical damage, convictions) which were examined in the original interview. The greater youthfulness of the non-contacts is consistent with the results of the one-year follow-up. The final results differ from that follow-up in one respect: the non-contacts at one-year follow-up were significantly more likely than other respondents to be not only young, but to have been convicted of alcohol-related offences. This was not so two to three years after the initial interviews. It may be that workers who are 'deviant' or unusual tend to leave their jobs, or to be 'shaken out' for whatever reason, at a quicker rate than men whose lifestyles are more placid, less disorganized. Perhaps the high rate of alcohol-related offences amongst the non-contacts at one-year follow-up was an indication that such offenders were especially likely to change their jobs and addresses frequently. Over two to three years, while non-contacts were still young, they became less atypical in other ways. These results are reassuring. While it is clearly a matter of regret that seventy-five men could not be contacted and twelve refused to be reinterviewed, there is no evidence that, apart from their youthfulness, they were different in other respects from those men who were reinterviewed two to three years after their inclusion in this study.

The final follow-up, like the interim exercise at one year, produced some fairly definite results; these are summarized below.

Conclusions from the two- to three-year follow-up

Two hundred and ten of the original 300 respondents were reinterviewed completely and partial information was collected from two more. As indicated by the one-year follow-up, considerable changes had occurred during the study period. The main conclusion, which was very clear, was that major changes in drinking habits had occurred in association with changes in job status. While such associations do not necessarily imply a cause-and-effect relationship, there is little doubt from the results that levels of alcohol consumption were largely determined by current occupational circumstances. Current job status was clearly related not only to the general level of alcohol consumption but also to the level of alcohol-related problems and to a range of perceptions of drinking levels and alcohol-related harm amongst one's workmates. Specifically, the main conclusions of the final follow-up interviews were:

1 Ten of the forty-six men who had left the drink trade had done so for reasons involving their own excessive drinking (nine) or that of their fellow workers (one).

2 Those remaining in alcohol production had maintained their higher level of alcohol consumption compared with those remaining in control-group employment. One of the controls reported that he was now an Alcoholics Anonymous member.

3 The stable alcohol producers retained their higher assessment of what constituted heavy beer drinking.

4 The stable alcohol producers remained significantly more likely than the stable controls to report drinking at work.

5 The stable alcohol producers remained significantly more likely than the stable controls to report that their workmates drank heavily.

6 While the stable alcohol producers were not more likely than the stable controls to report alcohol-related harm amongst their workmates they were more likely to allude to alcoholism, whereas the controls mainly referred to drunkenness.

7 The stable alcohol producers increased their alcohol-related problem scores. The stable controls did not.

8 There was no significant difference between the proportion of stable alcohol producers and stable controls experiencing new alcohol-related physical damage.

9 There was no significant difference between the proportions of stable alcohol producers and controls reporting either alcohol-related convictions, marital breakdowns, absenteeism, parasuicide during the study period, or admitting that they had alcohol-related problems, either past or present.

10 Those leavers who were working in control-group type jobs had reduced their average week's alcohol consumption by 30.9 per cent.

11 Those leavers who were unemployed had not significantly changed their consumption.

12 Control-group workers who were unemployed had increased their consumption by 54.7 per cent.

13 The leavers retained their original, high, assessments of what constituted heavy beer drinking in spite of their reduced alcohol consumption.

14 The leavers were less likely to drink at work or to perceive their workmates as heavy drinkers than were their stable counterparts.

15 The average problem score of the leavers had risen significantly, regardless of whether or not they were unemployed or working.

16 The average weekly alcohol consumption of the entrants had risen by 280.0 per cent.

17 In spite of their increased alcohol consumption, the entrants retained their original low assessment of what constituted heavy drinking.

18 The entrants were now more likely to report drinking at work, and to perceive their workmates as heavy drinkers or as being alcoholics.

19 The average problem score of the entrants was much higher than that of the stable alcohol producers and controls.

20 Two of the eight entrants reported that, in their view, they were now alcoholics.

21 Overall consumption changes amongst the 107 alcohol producers and 103 controls who were reinterviewed were not great. Both subgroups were drinking more. Virtually all meaningful changes related to current job status rather than to job status at first interview during 1975.

22 The ten heavy drinkers or self-identified alcoholics had been atypical at their original 1975 interviews in relation to their previous work records, particularly their high rate of previous employment in 'high-risk' jobs, their above-average levels of alcohol consumption, and their alcohol-related problem scores.

23 Those who refused to be reinterviewed, or who could not be contacted for reinterview, differed from those who were reinterviewed only in that they were significantly more likely to be aged twenty-five or less.

While these results are unequivocal, they are best accepted as indications, rather than as precise measures, of what had befallen the respondents during the study period. As indicated in Chapter 3, surveys do produce distorted results, and probably this one did too. Some of the practical advantages and problems of this study, together with some general conclusions, are discussed in the following chapter.

8 Conclusions
and discussion

This final chapter is concerned with some of the general empirical and theoretical conclusions to be drawn from the study described above. Some of these relate to the logistics of implementing such an exercise, others relate to the findings themselves.

The logistics of the longitudinal survey

Levels of response. Fieldwork revealed that this study had some fairly major advantages and disadvantages. At the outset discussions with managements and trade unions in the companies co-operating with this exercise paved the way for surprisingly successful initial data collection. An interview survey of this type would have been impossible without key management and trade union officials being involved, and being fully informed about the purpose and methods of the study. Pre-testing, piloting, and talks with people in the drink trade ensured that the interview itself was a fairly straightforward exercise. The initial interviewing in 1975 was all carried out during company time and on company premises. Even so, the co-operation of trade unions, and an explanatory letter on Medical Research Council stationery, made it clear to all concerned that the survey was not a management exercise and was confidential. The high initial response rate of 97.4 per cent owed much to the fact that interviewing was in company time and was widely accepted as an external, confidential exercise. In addition, it is probable that the response rate was so high because all of those interviewed were new recruits and were widely dispersed throughout the total work force of each of the co-operating companies.

A subsequent, separate, study had involved attempting to interview not only new recruits, but the entire work force, in other companies. Although a similar approach was adopted to that employed in the survey described above, only a minority of these work forces agreed to be interviewed. There appeared to be two reasons for this low response. First, unlike the survey described in this book, the researchers had no direct discussion with trade union officials. Information was only passed on to them by management. Second, and probably more important, once details of the impending survey were distributed (by a letter from the researchers) workers were able to discuss the study with their colleagues. Some were hostile to the idea of having their drinking habits examined and appear to have persuaded others not to co-operate. In one company a foreman was believed to have dissuaded his entire shift from participating.

In the present study, which dealt only with new recruits, most respondents were 'isolated' and did not have much chance to discuss their co-operation with others. The majority were interviewed very soon after beginning their new jobs and may well have felt too insecure in their new surroundings to refuse to co-operate. In any event, only eight men out of 308 did refuse.

While the initial response rate was very high, a large minority of those originally interviewed did subsequently drop out of the study. Very few of these did so by refusing, although some of the refusals appeared to be upset and defensive about their drinking when approached later. The main reason for depletion of the original cohort interviewed was the geographical and occupational mobility of the younger respondents. At the final follow-up, seventy-five men could no longer be traced. The initial (1975) interviews indicated that these non-contacts differed from other respondents only in their youthfulness and mobility. It is encouraging that the evidence did not show these men to be atypical in other ways, such as their drinking habits or alcohol-related problems. Could these men have been traced? At the beginning of this study each man provided two or more follow-up addresses. It would certainly have been possible to collect additional details which could have been used to increase the final contact rate. Each respondent could have been asked for his National Insurance and National Health numbers and for his precise date of birth (instead of simply year of birth). There is no doubt that fuller information could have been elicited to facilitate follow-up via institutional agencies if necessary. This has been done with great success, for example, in tracing British heroin users (Stimson *et al.* 1978). The subjects of this study were not a clinical group. They were ordinary workers. For this reason it was decided at an early stage in the investigation not to pursue any institutional means of follow-up. While this reduced the final contact rate, it was the method deemed appropriate for this type of study group. Other researchers should be aware that reliance upon forwarding addresses does have limitations, and may be advised to collect additional information so that they can follow respondents by other means if they so wish.

Reliability and validity

Data collected from individuals at different stages in the study showed that, on major items, respondents were extremely consistent (reliable) in their replies. As noted above, only recollection of alcohol-related problems appeared to be of doubtful reliability. This could indicate that respondents had short memories for many of the items included in that list (see *Appendix Ib*, question 13).

The validity (truthfulness) of the information collected by this survey is less certain. As described in Chapter 3, surveys of drinking behaviour appear to produce rather distorted results. It was widely noted during fieldwork that respondents warmed to the interview situation. Many continued to talk freely and informatively after the formal interview had been completed. Some of the most interesting anecdotal material was collected in this way. The majority of those interviewed clearly did not mind being included in the study. Most evidently enjoyed talking about their drinking to a neutral listener in a confidential setting. Moreover, there is no particular reason to suppose that men in either subgroup were very different in their willingness to provide honest information. Probably some did bias their replies, unintentionally or intentionally. In the absence of clear evidence about this we must assume that the data collected were distorted. Even so, one is left with some interesting and informative comparisons, even if one accepts, as one probably should, that the precise percentages cited in the previous three chapters are inaccurate.

Conclusions about drinking and alcohol-related problems

Drinking problems at work. Much of this book has been concerned with alcohol-related problems amongst different occupational groups. The survey showed clearly that not only levels of drinking but, in some cases, levels of alcohol-related problems vary greatly in different work settings. The great majority of the men interviewed in this study reported that, at some time, they had experienced some kind of alcohol-related problem, however minor. A minority reported getting into serious trouble with their drinking, falling foul of the law, being dismissed from their jobs, or encountering physical damage. A great deal of emphasis in presenting the preceding results has been placed on the fact that the alcohol producers drank more and experienced more problems with their drinking. It has also been observed that, even amongst the control group, alcohol-related problems were commonplace. While both of these statements are true, it is important to qualify them. The great majority of men in either subgroup appeared to be productive workers, leading healthy and, one hopes, happy lives. Only a handful of those interviewed reported having encountered problems that were obvious or important at work. Some had taken days off or had arrived late due to hangovers. Some had become physically incapacitated. Others had been warned by supervisors about the effects of their drinking and a few had been dismissed because of drunkenness and consequent inefficiency at work. It must be remembered that this study was confined to new recruits. Many of those interviewed, particularly those engaged in brewing, distilling, and other 'high-risk' jobs, asserted that the most serious drinking problems they saw at work were amongst men who had been in their jobs for a long time. Probably the full effects of 'high-risk' jobs on drinking habits take time to become evident. The fact that eight of the ten heavy drinkers or 'alcoholics' had previous records of 'high-risk' employment supports this probability. There seems no doubt that not only do a minority of men suffer from their drinking, but that sometimes these problems are evident at work. Certainly, a great deal of absenteeism and many industrial accidents are attributable to excessive drinking (Davies 1978; Hore 1977).

The great majority of alcohol-related problems reported by the study group did not appear to impinge directly upon their work. The main reason for this appeared to be the pattern of weekend drinking. Most respondents did much of their drinking at weekends. Typically, drinking occurred on Friday evenings and particularly on Saturdays. Thus many of the problems caused by a high alcohol intake in a single day were experienced either on Saturdays (after Friday) or on Sundays (after Saturday). Clearly many of those interviewed regarded Sunday as their traditional recovery day from their main drinking day, which was most commonly Saturday. Very early on the interviewers learned that it was not productive to attempt to carry out home interviews on Sunday mornings, since many men simply did not get out of bed until lunchtime. They were 'sleeping it off'. The fact that most of the heavy drinking and attendant problems occurred at weekends may explain why so many employers are unaware of the alcohol-related problems amongst their workers. The evidence of this study indicates that while some men do conspicuously allow their alcohol-related problems to become apparent at work, the great majority do not. In addition it is clear that there is far greater tolerance of drinking at work than official company rules indicate. There appeared to be very widespread support amongst manual workers in the alcohol production firms for drinking on the job. Moreover, not only was drinking itself accepted and even encouraged, but alcohol-related problems were widely tolerated and covered up. Several men stated that they sometimes 'filled-in' to do the work of colleagues who were the worse for wear after a heavy night's drinking. In addition, some senior company officials indicated that they sometimes felt obliged to 'carry' men whose excessive drinking was acknowledged to be a tragic occupational hazard, simply the results of working in close proximity to accessible alcohol.

While most workers appeared to keep their drinking problems away from their work, some did not. It is certain that some 'problem drinkers' or 'alcoholics' can be identified at work, and may thereby be put in touch with helping agencies, often with pleasing results (e.g. Kenyon 1977; Schramm 1977).

Determinants of drinking behaviour

People constantly modify their social behaviour to adapt to their surroundings. In the same week a man might drink to intoxication at a rugby club and sip sedately at a glass of wine in a restaurant. As indicated in Chapter 1 there is a considerable body of evidence which shows that different social groups have hugely varying ways of drinking. People change their drinking behaviour and attitudes to drinking enormously between infancy and maturity (e.g. Davies and Stacey 1972; Jahoda and Cramond 1972). Most people adapt their drinking behaviour to conform to that of their associates: company directors imbibe pink gins while their manual employees drink beer. For most people drinking is a convivial, social activity which they modify to suit the occasion and the company.

The study described in this book indicates unequivocally that people do change their drinking behaviour, often very considerably. Beyond doubt one major reason for such change is the individual's job situation. There are, of course, other influences apart from a person's job. Discussions with those interviewed in this study showed that some men identified very strongly with the *esprit de corps* of their workmates. They were 'one of the boys', and joined in with their drinking enthusiastically. Other men were much more reserved. Some were concerned at the possible dangers of being caught while drinking or intoxicated at work. Others were simply more interested in their wives and families than in joining in with daytime drinking. Many men simply conformed to whichever group they happened to be with at the time. This was clearly shown by the increase in drinking that followed a move from a 'low-risk' to a 'high-risk' job, or from a 'low-risk' job into unemployment, which evidently had similar results. On the strength of the evidence of this study, it would appear that, of the items examined, current occupation was the most influential in determining an individual's current drinking habits and consequent alcohol-related problems. Marriage may also have had a big effect, but the evidence for this was inconclusive. This investigation did not examine closely each respondent's 'reference groups'. These are individuals with whom a person identifies and who are adopted as models and exemplars. Even so, it is clear that the general level of drinking amongst the men in this study was determined by that of their work associates at any one time. It was also clearly shown that people very often varied their drinking habits simply because of the jobs they had, and because of the availability of, or pressure to drink, alcohol. Many men stated that they drank while working in a brewery or a distillery simply because alcohol was within easy reach. Some commented that if they had worked in a chocolate factory their chocolate consumption might have risen in just the same way.

There certainly was considerable encouragement to drink amongst men working in breweries and distilleries. A great deal of interesting anecdotal evidence to this effect was obtained. Whatever company policies were about drinking at work, men widely regarded illicit drinking as an enjoyable sporting activity which sometimes relieved the monotony of their jobs. Unofficial support appeared more influential than official restrictions in dictating the amount of illegal drinking. One brewery worker commented: 'It's a game really. Everybody knows what the rules are, but nearly everybody breaks them. You have to lie down drunk to get into trouble.'

Spontaneous remission

It is clear from the evidence of this study that many of those who become 'problem drinkers', if sufficiently motivated, are able to take positive action to reduce their drinking to more acceptable, less harmful levels. Several men reported having taken the major step of changing their jobs in order to relieve the pressures to drink during working hours. None of these men had been near any official treatment agency, yet several had clearly reduced their alcohol consumption levels and appeared to be much happier about their drinking. Clearly, some individuals do pay attention to danger signs indicating that they are drinking excessively.

This is an important conclusion, since the majority of individuals seeking help with their drinking from official agencies appear to do so only after a major tragedy has befallen them, such as a traffic accident, marital split, or dismissal from work. Treatment agencies, of course, only come into contact with an atypical minority of those with alcohol-related problems. It is reassuring to find that some of those in the community who do start to worry about their drinking resolve their problems without professional help. Significantly, all of those who reported leaving the drink trade to cut down their drinking cited a very definite motivating factor. For some, it was pressure from their wives, for others it was the importance of protecting their occupational prerequisite, a driving licence. All had clear and important reasons for drinking less. Other men seemed to lack such emotional or social support to adapt their drinking and in consequence were more influenced by their peers at work. One interpretation is that an individual will only modify his/her drinking behaviour if there is a good reason to do so, if a more attractive alternative exists. With drinking amongst younger men the alternative may well often be marriage, which provides a total change in lifestyle. Anecdotal information provided by many men indicated that they had drunk quite heavily while young and single, then reduced their consumption upon falling in love and establishing a new focus and lifestyle. Similarly, those reporting that they had encountered problems with their drinking invariably stated that such difficulties had been overcome for the sake of achieving some more important objective, such as the preservation of their family life. This is consistent with other evidence that the problem drinkers or alcoholics who have the best prognosis are those with the most adequate social support (e.g. Pattison 1966). Some men encountered serious alcohol-related problems and had resolved these. While there is no clear clinical evidence that any of these men had been 'alcoholics', they had certainly managed to move from problem drinking to problem-free(r) drinking. There is considerable evidence that, even amongst individuals treated for 'alcoholism', some later return to problem-free, 'controlled', or social drinking (e.g. Lloyd and Salzberg 1975; Miller and Muñoz 1976; Smart 1978). Probably, as has been suggested by Armor, Polich, and Stambull (1976), it is more important that a person chooses to change his harmful drinking than whether that individual decides to abstain or to reduce his consumption. This study supports the view that an individual's drinking habits and alcohol-related problems are not necessarily lasting, and may be ameliorated if that person is so motivated or enters a *milieu* where the pressures to drink are reduced.

Drinking amongst male manual workers

The evidence of this study does indicate some general conclusions about drinking amongst working men. The overwhelming majority of those included in this study drank alcohol regularly, regardless of their employment. Drinking was a major part of their weekend activities and was clearly taken quite seriously by many. While considerable comment has already been made in the preceding chapters, a few points are worth amplifying.

First, there appeared to be widespread misconceptions about alcoholic beverages, even amongst men engaged in the drink trade. Many men clearly had little idea about the effects of what they themselves drank. One especially commonplace area of ignorance was the belief that spirits are far stronger than in fact they are, and that beer, lager, etc. are much weaker than in fact they are. Several men, in informal discussions, stated that in their view anybody drinking 'only' beer could not be regarded as a 'serious' or 'problem' drinker, and certainly never an alcoholic. Others stated with equal conviction that anybody drinking spirits was, by definition, a heavy drinker. Perhaps this type of misconception usefully could be the target of a future health education campaign. There is, of course, no evidence that giving people accurate information will necessarily make them act sensibly, but it may help.

Second, drinking appeared to have many of the attributes of a sporting activity. It was quite an important aspect of many men's lives, and, like certain sports, carried risks that were accepted by the participants. In addition, drinking was clearly often competitive. Men liked to keep up with their peers, to drink as much and not to be left out. Many of the alcohol-related problems examined in this investigation were clearly not regarded by many men as cause for concern. This is a good instance of a researcher defining 'a problem' in a very different way from his subjects. While many respondents reported having been convicted of alcohol-related offences, suffering from gastritis, or missing working days due to their drinking, only a minority were prepared to concede that their drinking had ever caused them problems. They accepted certain alcohol-related difficulties either as minor irritations on the way to some greater benefit, or regarded them as some kind of 'battle honour'. Some of the younger men appeared quite amused about their brushes with the law, arguments, and hangovers. Such things were much discussed amongst themselves, and, within certain groups, appeared to carry considerable prestige, rather like duelling scars in pre-War Germany.

As Davies and Stacey (1972) have shown, the drinker is commonly esteemed as a sociable individual. There is no doubt that drinking was a major pursuit amongst the study group, especially amongst the younger men. It is perhaps a matter of concern that the prevailing attitudes to drinking amongst these Edinburgh workers were so very accepting of quite a range of alcohol-related 'problems'.

Drunkenness was clearly tolerated quite widely, even though 'alcoholism' was regarded as pitiful or, at least, as unacceptable. Presumably drunkenness behaviour is so commonplace in Scotland because social attitudes are so lenient towards it. This is not a new observation. The Scottish Health Education Unit mounted a television campaign during 1978 to help to counteract the image of the drunk as an amusing or admirable figure. Drinking habits and attitudes to drinking are deeply entrenched in tradition. It is doubtful that there are easy solutions to alcohol-related problems so long as large sections of the community do not distinguish between drinking which is problem-free, and that which is not.

Pre-selection or availability?

The two primary aims of the study described in this book were to ascertain whether high-risk jobs *attracted* heavy drinkers or alcoholics, or whether they 'produced' them due to the availability of alcohol.

The results show that the drink trade did recruit more than its fair share of men with poor work records or who were already heavy drinkers. It could be argued that, since the study group were in their new jobs when first interviewed, their drinking levels were already the results of their new work environment. Perhaps this was so, although most of the new recruits stated that their previous week's consumption had been typical of their usual weekly intake. In spite of this uncertainty, the poorer work records of recruits to the drink trade are consistent with the theory that 'high-risk' jobs do pre-select or recruit men somehow especially likely to drink heavily.

It was clear that entry into a 'high-risk' work environment led to generally higher levels of alcohol consumption and often to higher levels of alcohol-related problems. The drink-trade workers were consistently more likely to perceive their working situations as being characterized by heavy drinking and to notice alcohol dependence amongst their workmates. Drinking behaviour and many other related factors did demonstrably alter in association with job changes, as shown by those moving between 'high-risk' and 'low-risk' jobs or becoming unemployed. The likely explanation for such changes appear to be the availability of alcohol and the level of encouragement or coercion to drink it.

In conclusion, this study showed that one particular high-risk industry in one city did recruit a particular type of worker and that movement from one job environment to another may dictate not only drinking habits but also alcohol-related problems.

Appendix 1
The interview schedules

(a) THE MAIN SCHEDULE

All 300 respondents were initially interviewed using a twenty-one-page schedule. The questions included in this main schedule are summarized below.

1 What is your job? Please could you tell me what your work involves?
2 How long have you been working here?
3(a) Do you work shifts?
  (b) (*If 'yes'*:) Do you work one set shift, e.g. night shift, or are you on a rota?
  (c) (*If on rota*:) How frequently does the rota change?
  (d) Does working shifts disrupt your life in any way?
  (e) (*If 'yes'*:) How are you affected?
  (f) Do you think a different system of shifts, i.e. more/less frequent rotating, would be more satisfactory?
  (g) (*If 'yes'*:) What system would you like?
4 Are there any things you particularly like about your job?
5 Are there any things that you dislike about your job?
6 What other jobs have you had in the past? Could you tell me about them starting with the first job you had? (*Record job type and duration.*)
7 Have you ever worked as a barman or in a pub/hotel or licenced club?

8   Have you ever been in the Army, Navy, Air Force?

9   Have you ever worked on a merchant ship?

10   Why did you apply for this job? Was there anything about the firm or the work that particularly appealed to you?

11   Have either of your parents done the same sort of work?

12   Have any of your brothers and sisters done the same sort of work?

13(a)   Have you ever been out of work?

(b)   (*If 'yes'*:) What is the longest period you have been out of work?

(c)   (*If 'yes'*:) Why were you out of work?

14   What sort of work does/did your father do? (*Record whether manual or non-manual.*)

15   At what age did you leave school?

16   Have you passed any exams?

17(a)   Do you smoke?

(b)   (*If 'yes'*:) Which do you smoke mainly, cigarettes, cigars, or a pipe?

(c)   About how many cigarettes (cigars) do you smoke each day?

(d)   About how much tobacco do you smoke in a week?

18   How many days a week do you usually have a drink?

19   (*If answer to 18 is less than weekly*:) How many days a month/year do you have a drink?

20(a)   (*If respondent does not drink alcohol*:) Are there any occasions when you do drink alcohol?

Not even at Christmas or New Year?

Not even at parties?

Celebrations?

Not even the occasional sherry or shandy?

(b)   Now I am going to read you some of the reasons which people give for not drinking. Can you in each case, just say 'yes' or 'no' according to whether it is one of the reasons you yourself would give?

(i) I don't drink because of personal conviction.

(ii) I don't drink because I don't like it.

(iii) I don't drink because of health reasons.

(iv) I don't drink because of the high cost.

(v) I don't drink because most of my friends don't care for drinking.

(vi) I don't really care whether I drink or not.

(viii) Any other reasons? (*Specify.*)

(viii) (*Not to be read out:*) *Subject is abstinent alcoholic.*

(ix) *Refused to answer.*

(x) *Answer otherwise not obtained.*

21(a) Have you ever during the last twelve months had even one drink of beer?

(b) (*If 'yes':*) How many days a week do you usually drink beer?

(c-d) (*If answer to (b) is less than weekly:*) How many days a month/year do you usually drink beer?

(e) When did you last have a drink of beer?

(f) What is the usual amount of beer that you drink at one time?

22 *As for 21 but related to spirits.*

23 *As for 21 but related to wines.*

24 Can you remember exactly what you have drunk on each day during the last week? (*To be recorded in units.*)

25(a) Would you say that last week was fairly typical of what you usually have to drink in a week?

(b) (*If answer to (a) is 'no':*) So would you say you had more or less than usual to drink last week? (*Record number of units more/less than usual.*)

26 How old would you say you were when you started drinking as opposed to just trying out drinks to see what they were like?

27(a) Do you think there were any reasons why you started drinking at that age?

(b) Was there any particular person or set of people with whom you used to drink at that time?

28(a) How many pints of beer would a man need to drink in a week to count as a heavy drinker?

(b) How many bottles of spirits would a man need to drink in a week to count as a heavy drinker?

(c) Up to what number of pints of beer could a man drink in a week and still be a light drinker?

(d) Up to what amount of spirits could a man drink in a week and still be a light drinker?

29(a) People have different feelings about the amount they would like to drink. Could you tell me which of these statements comes closest to the way you feel?

(i) I wish I could afford to drink more than I do now.

(ii) I'm perfectly satisfied with the amount I drink now.

(iii) I sometimes feel I should drink a bit less than I do.

(iv) I would definitely like to cut down the amount I drink.

(b) Have you ever tried to cut down your drinking at all?

30 Can you guess what your own drinking costs on average a week? By your own drinking I mean the cost of what you actually drink, whether you pay for it or someone else buys it for you. Don't include the cost of drink you buy for other people.

31 Were you once a heavier drinker than you are now?

32 Since you started working here have you drunk any more or less than you did before?

33(a) The last time you were in a pub, how long did you stay there?

(b) Was that a longer time or a shorter time than you usually stay when you visit a pub?

(c) (*If 'longer' or 'shorter'*:) How long do you usually spend in a pub?

34(a) How often do you drink in any of the following:

      (i) pub

     (ii) licenced club

    (iii) work

    (iv) restaurants

     (v) other people's homes

    (vi) own home.

(b) What proportion of your drinking would you say you do in public houses?

35 ·Have you ever had any of the following:

      (i) liver trouble — cirrhosis or enlarged liver

     (ii) stomach ulcer

    (iii) TB of the chest.

36(a) Have people annoyed you by criticizing your drinking?

(b) Have you ever had problems at work because of your drinking?

(c) Has your doctor ever advised you not to drink as much as you do?

(d) Have you ever spent more money than you ought to on drink?

(e) Have you ever had trouble or quarrels with family or friends because of your drinking?

(f) Have you ever had health problems because of your drinking?

(g) Have you ever had financial problems because of your drinking?

(h) Have you ever been in a road accident (as driver or pedestrian) because of your drinking?

(i) Have you ever been in other accidents (home/work) because of your drinking?

(j) Have you ever had a drink first thing in the morning to steady your nerves or to get rid of a hangover?

(k) After drinking have you found your hand shaky in the morning?

(l) Have you ever arrived late at work due to a hangover?

(m) Have you ever missed a day's work due to a hangover?

(n) After drinking have you ever found you can't remember the night before?

(o) Have you ever gone without a drink for a period to prove you can do so?

(p) Do you ever find that when you start drinking you can't stop?

(q) Have you ever had special medical treatment for drinking?

(r) Have you ever 'heard' or 'seen' things due to drinking?

37(a) In your present job do you ever drink at work?

(b) (*If 'yes' to (a)*:) On what sort of occasion do you drink at work?

(c) On about how many days during an average week or month do you drink at work?

(d) Do you get alcoholic drinks free or at special discount as a part of your job?

38(a) Some people's religious views are connected to their opinions on drinking. Do you belong to any religious denomination or group?

(b) (*If 'yes'*:) What is that?

(c) Do you go to church, synagogue, etc.?

(d) (*If 'yes'*:) How often do you usually go to church, synagogue, or your place of worship?

(e) Do your religious views effect your drinking?

(f) (*If 'yes'*:) How do your religious views affect your drinking? Do they make you drink more or less?

39(a) Do any of the people you work with drink much more than you?

(b) Are any of the people you work with heavy drinkers?

(c) (*If 'yes'*:) What proportion of the people you work with are heavy drinkers?

(d) Do any of the people you work with suffer because of their drinking?

(e) (*If 'yes':*) In what way do they suffer?

40(a) Have you ever had any serious illnesses?

(b) (*If 'yes':*) What was this, please?

(c) Have you ever had trouble with your nerves?

(d) Have you ever taken an overdose?

41(a) Does your wife/fiancée/girlfriend drink alcohol?

(b) (*If 'yes':*) Has her drinking caused any problems?

42 Has your wife/fiancée/girlfriend ever had trouble with her nerves?

43(a) Does/did your mother/stepmother drink alcohol?

(b) (*If 'yes':*) Has her drinking caused any problems?

44(a) Does/did your father/stepfather drink alcohol?

(b) (*If 'yes':*) Has his drinking caused any problems?

45 Have either of your parents/stepparents had to consult a doctor because of their drinking?

46 Have you ever been in trouble with the police? (*Record any convictions fully.*)

47 Do you have any special hobby or pastime?

48 How long have you lived at your present address?

49 How many addresses have you lived in during the past five years?

50 Where were you born?

51 When were you born?

52 How many people live in your household?

53. How many rooms does your household have (excluding kitchens and bathrooms)?

54 Is your housing rented from the Council, privately rented unfurnished, etc.? (*Specify.*)

55 *Classify type of accommodation, e.g. flat, bedsitter, etc.*

56(a) Did you live with both parents all the time until you were sixteen?

(b) (*If 'no':*) Why was this?

(c) (*If either parent has died:*) How old were you when he/she/they died?

57 Are you living with ... parents:
father and stepmother
mother and stepfather
mother

father
grandparents
other guardians
none of these.

58   Are you married?

59(a) Have you been married before?

  (b) (*If 'yes':*) What happened to your partner? Is she still alive?

60(a) Has anybody close to you, such as a brother, sister, relative, or friend, died recently?

  (b) (*If 'yes':*) Will you tell me about this, please?

61   How old is your wife/fiancée/girlfriend?

62   How much money did you pick up last week?

63   Is that what you usually earn?

At the end of the interview the respondent was asked whether or not he was willing to be reinterviewed one or two years later. Those agreeable to this were asked to provide details of at least two forwarding addresses where they could be contacted.

(b) THE SHORTENED INTERVIEW SCHEDULE

During the follow-up of respondents one year and two to two-and-a-half years after the initial interview, the following shortened and amended schedule was used.

1(a) Do you smoke?
  (b) (*If 'yes'*:) Which do you mainly smoke, cigarettes, cigars, or a pipe?
  (c) About how many cigarettes (cigars) do you smoke each day?
  (d) About how much tobacco do you smoke each week?
2   How many days each week do you usually have a drink?
3(a) (*If answer to 2 was less than weekly*:) How many days a month/year do you have a drink?
  (b) When did you last have a drink?
4   (*If respondent does not drink alcohol*:) Are there any occasions when you do drink alcohol?
       Not even at Christmas or New Year?
       Not even at parties?
       Celebrations?
       Not even the occasional sherry or shandy?
5   Now I am going to read you some of the reasons which people give for not drinking. Can you, in each case, just say 'yes' or 'no' according to whether it is one of the reasons you yourself would give?
       (i) I don't drink because of personal conviction.

    (ii) I don't drink because I don't like it.

   (iii) I don't drink because of health reasons.

   (iv) I don't drink because of the high cost.

    (v) I don't drink because most of my friends don't care for drinking.

   (vi) I don't really care whether I drink or not.

  (vii) Any other reasons? (*specify*.)

 (viii) (*Not to be read out*:) *Subject is an abstinent alcoholic* (*only to be used if admitted incidentally*).

   (ix) *Refused to answer.*

    (x) *Answer otherwise not obtained.*

6   Can you remember exactly what you have drunk on each day during the last week?

7(a) Would you say that last week was fairly typical of what you usually have to drink in a week?

 (b) (*If 'no'*:) Would you say you had more or less than usual to drink last week?

 (c) How much more/less than usual did you have to drink last week?

8(a) How many pints of beer would a man have to drink in a week to count as a heavy drinker?

 (b) How many bottles of spirits would a man have to drink in a week to count as a heavy drinker?

 (c) Up to what number of pints of beer could a man drink in a week and still be a light drinker?

 (d) Up to what amount of spirits could a man drink in a week and still be a light drinker?

9   Can you guess what your own drinking costs in an average week? By your own drinking, I mean the cost of what you actually drink, whether you pay for it or someone else buys it for you. Don't include the cost of drink you buy for someone else.

10   (*To be asked only if respondents still at original* (1975) *company*:) Since you started working here have you drunk any more or less than you did before?

11   Have you ever had any of the following:

    (i) Gastritis (inflamed stomach)

   (ii) liver trouble — cirrhosis or enlarged liver

  (iii) stomach ulcer

  (iv) TB of chest.

12(a) Have you had any days off work during the past four weeks? (*Excluding holidays.*)

  (b) (*If 'yes':*) Why was this, please?

13(a) Have people annoyed you by criticizing your drinking?

  (b) Have you ever had problems at work because of your drinking?

  (c) Has your doctor ever advised you not to drink as much as you do?

  (d) Have you ever spent more money than you ought to on drink?

  (e) Have you ever had trouble or quarrels with family or friends because of your drinking?

  (f) Have you ever had health problems because of your drinking?

  (g) Have you ever had financial problems because of your drinking?

  (h) Have you ever been in a road accident (as driver or pedestrian) because of your drinking?

  (i) Have you ever been in other accidents (home/work) because of your drinking?

  (j) Have you ever had a drink first thing in the morning to steady your nerves or to get rid of a hangover?

  (k) After drinking have you found your hand shaky in the morning?

  (l) Have you ever arrived late at work due to a hangover?

  (m) Have you ever missed a day's work due to a hangover?

  (n) After drinking have you ever found you can't remember the night before?

  (o) Have you ever gone without a drink for a period to prove you can do so?

  (p) Do you ever find that when you start drinking you can't stop?

  (q) Have you ever had special medical treatment for drinking?

  (r) Have you ever 'heard' or 'seen' things due to drinking?

14(a) In your present job do you ever drink during working hours?

  (b) (*If 'yes':*) On what sorts of occasions do you drink at work?

  (c) On about how many days during an average week/month do you drink at work?

15(a) Do any of the people you work with drink much more than you?

  (b) Are any of the people you work with heavy drinkers?

(c) (*If 'yes':*) What proportion of the people you work with are heavy drinkers?

(d) Do any of the people you work with suffer because of their drinking?

(e) (*If 'yes':*) In what ways do they suffer?

16 Have you ever had trouble with your nerves?

17 Have you ever taken an overdose?

18(a) Has there ever been a period in your life when drinking has caused you problems?

(b) (*If 'yes':*) Is drinking causing you problems at present?
(*If 'yes' to (a) or (b):*) What kinds of problems has drinking caused you?

19 Have you ever been in trouble with the police? (*Record any convictions fully.*)

20(a) Are you married?

(b) Have you been married before?

(c) (*If 'yes':*) What happened to your partner? Is she still alive?

21 *Record whether respondent is still working for original company.*

22(a) (*If 'no':*) Why did you leave?

(b) (*If respondent was dismissed:*) Why were you dismissed?

22 What job are you doing now?

23(a) How much money did you pick up last week?

(b) Is that what you usually earn?

Bibliography

The following bibliography lists the main references that were useful in writing this book. Most, though not all, are referred to directly in the text.

A'Brook, M.F., Hailstone, J.D., and McLauchlan, I.E.J. (1967) Psychiatric Illness in the Medical Profession. *British Journal of Psychiatry* 113: 1013-23.

Amark, C. (1970) A Study of Alcoholism. *Acta Psychiatrica et Neurologica* Supplementum 70: 237-43.

Archer, J. (1977) Occupational Alcoholism. In, Schramm, C.J. (ed.) *Alcoholism and its Treatment in Industry*. Baltimore: Johns Hopkins University Press, 2-28.

Armor, D.J., Polich, J.M., and Stambull, H.B. (1976) *Alcoholism and Treatment*. Santa Monica, California: Rand Corporation.

Arner, O. (1973) The Role of Alcohol in Fatal Accidents Amongst Seamen. *British Journal of Addiction* 68: 185-89.

Arthur, R.J. (1965) The Naval Medical Officer as a Psychiatric Patient. *American Journal of Psychiatry* 122: 290-94.

Ashley, M.J., Ohlin, J.S., le Riche, W.H., Komaczewski, A., Schmidt, W., and Rankin, J.G. (1967) 'Continuous' and 'Intermittent' Alcoholics: A Comparison of Sociological and Physical Disease Characteristics in Relation to the Pattern of Drinking. *Addictive Diseases* 2(3): 515-32.

Barrett, T.M. (1943) Chronic Alcoholism in Veterans. *Quarterly Journal of Studies on Alcohol* 1: 68-78.

Beyer, H.G. (1908) International Congress for the Prevention of Alcoholism. *United States Naval Medical Bulletin* April 2: 86-92.

Board of Trade (1969) *Trawler Safety.* Final Report of the Committee of Inquiry into Trawler Safety. London: HMSO.

Bressler, B. (1976) Suicide and Drug Abuse in the Medical Community. *Suicide and Life—Threatening Behaviour* 6(3): 169-78.

Brun-Gulbrandsen, S. and Irgens-Jensen, O. (1967) Abuse of Alcohol Amongst Seamen. *British Journal of Addiction* 62: 19-27.

Butts, H. (1910) Insanity in the Navy. *United States Naval Medical Bulletin* 4: 459-75.

Cahalan, D. and Cisin, I.H. (1966) American Drinking Practices: Summary of Findings from a National Probability Sample: II Measurement of Massed Versus Spaced Drinking. *Quarterly Journal of Studies on Alcohol* 29: 130-54, 642, 658.

———(1975) *Final Report on a Service-Wide Survey of Attitudes and Behaviour of Naval Personnel Concerning Alcohol and Problem Drinking.* Washington: Bureau of Social Science Research Inc.

Cahalan, D. and Room, R. (1972) Problem Drinking Among American Men Aged 21-59. *American Journal of Public Health* 62: 1473-82.

———(1974) *Problem Drinking Among American Men.* New Brunswick, New Jersey: Publications Division, Rutgers Center of Alcohol Studies.

Carney, M.W.P. (1963) Alcoholic Hallucinosis Among Servicemen in Cyprus. *Journal of the Royal Army Medical Corps* 109: 164-70.

Carney, M.W.P. and Lawes, T.G.G. (1967) The Etiology of Alcoholism in the English Upper Classes. *Quarterly Journal of Studies on Alcohol* 28: 59-69.

Cartwright, A., Shaw, S., and Spratley, T.A. (1976) *Changing Patterns of Drinking Parts I and II.* London: Maudsley Pilot Project.

Cavan, S. (1966) *Liquor License: An Ethnography of Bar Behaviour.* Chicago: Aldine.

Clark, R.E. (1949) The Relationship of Alcoholic Psychosis

Commitment Rates to Occupational Income and Occupational Prestige. *American Sociological Review* 14: 539-43.

Council on Mental Health (1973) The Sick Physician. *Journal of the American Medical Association* 223: 684.

Cox, A., Rutter, M., Yule, B., and Quinton, D. (1977) Bias Resulting From Missing Information: Some Epidemiological Findings. *British Journal of Preventive and Social Medicine* 31: 131-36.

Cutler, R.E. and Storm, T. (1973) *Drinking Practices in Three British Columbia Cities: II Student Survey.* Vancouver: Alcoholism Foundation of British Columbia.

_____(1975) Observational Study of Alcohol Consumption in Natural Settings. *Journal of Studies on Alcohol* 36: 1173-83.

Davies, D.L. (1962) Normal Drinking in Recovered Alcoholics. *Quarterly Journal of Studies on Alcohol* 23: 94-104.

Davies, J. (1978) *Alcohol and Work.* Unpublished report. Personal communication.

Davies, J. and Stacey, B. (1972) *Teenagers and Alcohol: A developmental study in Glasgow* (Vol. II). London: HMSO.

Delahaye, S. (1977) An Analysis of Clients Using Alcoholic Agencies Within One Community Service. In, Madden, J.S., Walker, R., and Kenyon, W.H. (eds) *Alcoholism and Drug Dependence: A Multi-disciplinary Approach.* New York: Plenum, 335-54.

de Lint, J. and Schmidt, W. (1971) Consumption Averages and Alcoholism Prevalence: A Brief Review of Epidemiological Investigations. *British Journal of Addiction* 66: 97-107.

Department of Trade (1975) *Report of the Working Group on Discipline in the Fishing Industry.* London: HMSO.

Dight, S. (1976) *Scottish Drinking Habits.* London: Office of Population Censuses and Surveys, Social Survey Division, HMSO.

Donnan, S. and Haskey, J. (1977) Alcoholism and Cirrhosis of the Liver. *Population Trends* 7 Spring: 18-24.

Donnan, S. (1978) Personal communication.

Duffy, J. (1977) Alcohol Consumption, Alcoholism and Excessive Drinking — Errors in Estimates of Consumption Figures. *International Journal of Epidemiology* 6(4): 375-79.

Duffy, J.C. and Litin, E.M. (1964) Psychiatric Morbidity of Physicians. *Journal of the American Medical Association* 189: 989-92.

Edwards, D. (1973) Prediction of Success for Alcoholics in the Navy: A First Look *Journal of Clinical Psychology* 29 January: 86-9.

Edwards, G. (1975) The Alcoholic Doctor: A Case of Neglect. *Lancet* December 27: 1297-98.

Edwards, G., Chandler, J. and Hensman, C. (1972) Drinking in a London Suburb, I. *Quarterly Journal of Studies on Alcohol* Supplement 6: 69-93.

Edwards, G., Gross, M.M., Keller, M., Moser, J., and Room, R. (eds) (1977) *Alcohol-Related Disabilities*. Geneva: World Health Organization Offset Publication No. 32.

Edwards, G., Hawker, A., Hensman, C., Peto, J., and Williamson, V. (1973) Alcoholics Known and Unknown to Agencies: Epidemiological Studies in a London Suburb. *British Journal of Psychiatry* 123: 169-83.

Edwards, G., Kyle, E., and Nicholls, P. (1974) Alcoholics Admitted to Four Hospitals in England: I: Social Class and Interaction of Alcoholics With the Treatment System. *Quarterly Journal of Studies on Alcohol* 35: 499-522.

Einstein, S. (1975) *Beyond Drugs*. New York: Pergamon.

Fox, J. (1957) Narcotic Addiction Amongst Physicians. *Journal of the Michigan Medical Society* 56: 2.

Frank, H., Heil, W., and Leadolter, I. (1967) The Liver and Beer Consumption. *Münchener Medizinische Wochenschrift* 109: 892-97.

Franklin, R.A. (1977) One Hundred Doctors at the Retreat. *British Journal of Psychiatry* 131: 11-14.

Glatt, M.M. (1967) Complications of Alcoholism in the Social Sphere. *British Journal of Addiction* 62: 35-44.

____(1974) Alcoholism Among Doctors. *Lancet* 2: 342.

____(1976) The Alcoholic Doctor. *Lancet* 1: 196.

Gomberg, E.S. (1975) Prevalence of Alcoholism Among Ward Patients in a Veterans' Administration Hospital. *Journal of Studies on Alcohol* 36(11): 1458-67.

Grant, M. (1976) *Understanding Alcohol and Alcoholism in Scotland*. Edinburgh: Scottish Health Education Unit.

Grant, M. and Gwinner, P.D.V. (eds) (1979) *Alcoholism in Perspective*. London: Croom Helm

Gunderson, E.K.E. and Rahe, R.H. (1974) *Life Stress and Illness*. Springfield: Charles C. Thomas.

Gunderson, E.K.E. and Schukit, M.A. (1975) Hospitalization Rates for Alcoholism in the Navy and Marine Corps. *Diseases of the Nervous System* 36: 681-84.

Gwinner, P.D.V. (1976) The Treatment of Alcoholics in a Military Context. *Journal of Alcoholism* 11 (1): 24-31.

Harrington, L.G. and Price, A.C. (1962) Alcoholism in a Geriatric Setting. *Journal of the American Geriatric Society* 10: 197-211.

Hawker, A. (1978) *Adolescents and Alcohol*. London: Edsall.

Heath, D.B. (1962) Drinking Patterns of the Bolivian Camba. In, Pittman, D.J. and Snyder, C.R. (eds) *Society, Culture and Drinking Patterns*. New York: John Wiley, 22-36.

Heath, R.G. (1945) Group Psychotherapy and Alcohol Addiction. *Quarterly Journal of Studies on Alcohol* 5: 555-62.

Hitz, D. (1973) Drunken Sailors and Others: Drinking Problems in Specific Occupations. *Quarterly Journal of Studies on Alcohol* 34: 496-505.

Hochwald, H. (1951) The Occupational Performance of 30 Alcoholic Men. *Quarterly Journal of Studies on Alcohol* 12: 612-20.

Hood, R. and Sparks, R. (1970) *Key Issues in Criminology*. London: World University Library.

Hore, B.D. (1977) Alcohol and Alcoholism — Their Impact on Work. In, Grant, M. and Kenyon, W.H. (eds) *Alcoholism and Industry*. London: Alcohol Education Centre/Merseyside, Lancashire and Cheshire Council on Alcoholism, 34-40.

Hore, B.D. and Smith, E. (1973) Who Goes to Alcoholic Units? Paper Presented at Institute for Prevention and Treatment of Alcoholism, Belgrade.

Hughes, J.P.W. (1975) Alcoholism in Industry. *Medicine, Science and Law* 15 (1): 22-7.

J.I.F. (1947) Alcoholism: An Occupational Disease of Seamen. *Quarterly Journal of Studies on Alcohol* 8: 498-505.

Jahoda, G. and Cramond, J. (1972) *Children and Alcohol: A developmental study in Glasgow* (Vol. I). London: HMSO.

Jellinek, E.M. (1951) In, World Health Organization, Expert Committee on Mental Health *Report of First Session of the Alcoholism Subcommittee*. Geneva: WHO, Technical Report Series No. 42.

Jellinek, E.M. (1960) *The Disease Concept of Alcoholism*. Newhaven: Hillhouse Press.

156   *Drinking Careers*

Keevil, J.J. (1958) *Medicine and the Navy 1200-1900.* Edinburgh: E. and S. Livingstone Ltd.

Kessel, N. and Walton, H. (1974) *Alcoholism.* Harmondsworth: Pelican.

Kessler, M. and Gomberg, G. (1974) Observations of Barroom Drinking: Methodology and Preliminary Results. *Quarterly Journal of Studies on Alcohol* 35: 1392-96.

Kenyon, W.H. (1977) Policies and Programmes. In, Grant, M. and Kenyon, W.H. (eds) *Alcoholism and Industry.* London: Alcohol Education Centre/Merseyside, Lancashire and Cheshire Council on Alcoholism, 46-51.

Kolb, D. (1976) Prognostic Indicators for Black and White Alcoholics in the United States Navy. *Journal of Studies on Alcohol* 37 (7): 890-99.

Kolb, D. and Gunderson, E.K.E. (1977) Alcoholism in the United States Navy. *Armed Forces and Society* 3 (2): 183-94.

Krasner, N. (1978) Clinical Aspects of Alcohol-Induced Liver Disease. Paper presented at 4th International Conference on Alcoholism and Drug Dependence, Liverpool, April 11.

Kreitman, N. (1976) Limitations of Evidence. Paper presented at Symposium on Alcoholism: Advances in Medical and Psychiatric Understanding, London.

____(ed.) (1977) *Parasuicide.* London: Wiley.

Ledermann, S. (1956) Alcool, Alcoolisme, Alcoolisation: Données Scientifiques de Caratère Physiologique, Economique et Social. *Institut National d'Etudes Demographiques, Travaux et Documents,* Cahier No. 29. Paris: Presses Universitaires de France.

Lemere, F., Maxwell, M.A., and O'Hollaren, P. (1956) Sociological Survey of 7,828 Patients Treated for Alcoholism. *Journal of Nervous and Mental Disorders* 123: 281-85.

Lloyd, R.W. and Salzberg, H.C. (1975) Controlled Social Drinking: An Alternative to Abstinence as a Treatment Goal for Some Social Drinkers. *Psychological Bulletin* 82 (6): 815-42.

Long, J.R., Hewitt, L.E., and Blane, H.T. (1976) Alcohol Abuse in the Armed Services: A Review: I Policies and Programmes. *Military Medicine* 141 (12), December: 844-50.

____(1977) Alcohol Abuse in the Armed Services: A Review: II Problem Areas and Recommendations. *Military Medicine* 142 (2) February: 116-17, 120-28.

Ludlam, J.E. (1976) Physician Rehabilitation: A Better Alternative to Punishment. *Hospital Medical Staff* 5 (4): 8-11.

McDowall, R.J.S. (1971) *The Whiskies of Scotland*. London: John Murray.

Makela, K. (1977) Level of Consumption and Social Consequences of Drinking. Paper presented at Seminar on the Medico-Social Risks of Alcohol Consumption. Luxembourg-Kironsberg, November 16 to 18.

Maletsky, B.M. and Klotter, J. (1975) The Prevalence of Alcoholism in a Military Hospital *Military Medicine* 140 (4) April 273-75.

Marjot, D. (1970) Alcoholic Psychosis. *Journal of the Royal Naval Medical Service* 41: 124.

Mayer, J. and Myerson, D.J. (1970) Characteristics of Out-patient Alcoholics in Relation to Change in Drinking, Work and Marital Status During Treatment. *Quarterly Journal of Studies on Alcohol* 31: 889-97.

Mellor, C.S. (1967) The Epidemiology of Alcoholism. *Hospital Medicine* December: 284-94.

Merseyside Council on Alcoholism (1973) *The Alcohol Explosion*. Tenth Annual Report.

Miller, P.M., Ingham, J.G., Plant, M.A., and Miller, T.I. (1977) Alcohol Consumption and Self-Disclosure. *British Journal of Addiction* 72 (4) December: 296-300.

Miller, W. and Muñoz, R. (1976) *How to Control Your Drinking*. Englewood Cliffs, NJ: Prentice-Hall.

Moss, M.C. and Beresford-Davies, E.B. (1967) *A Survey of Alcoholism in an English County*. London: Geigy Scientific Publications.

Murray, R.M. (1975) Alcoholism and Employment. *Journal of Alcoholism* 10: 23-6.

——(1976) Alcoholism Amongst Male Doctors in Scotland. *Lancet* October 2: 729-31.

Noie, N. (1977) Medicine's Response to the Disabled Doctor Problem: Help Our Colleagues, Protect Their Patients. *Hospital Medical Staff* 6 (4): 9-14.

O'Connor, J. (1978) *The Young Drinkers*. London: Tavistock.

Office of Population Censuses and Surveys (1978) *1970-1972 Occupational Mortality*, decennial supplement. London: HMSO.

Pattison, E.M. (1966) A Critique of Alcoholism Treatment Concepts: With Special Reference to Abstinence. *Quarterly Journal of Studies on Alcohol* 27: 49-77.

Pernanen, K. (1974) Validity of Survey Data on Alcohol Use. In, Gibbins, R.J. *et al.* (eds) *Alcohol and Drug Problems.* New York: John Wiley, 355-74.

Pittman, D.J. (1967) International Overview: Social and Cultural Factors in Drinking Patterns, Pathological and Non-Pathological. In, Pittman, D.J. (ed.) *Alcoholism.* New York: Harper and Row.

Pittman, D.J. and Snyder, C.R. (1972) *Society, Culture and Drinking Patterns.* London: Wiley.

Plant, M.A. (1975) Alcoholism in Scotland. *New Psychiatry* 2 (25) December 13: 12-13.

____(1975) *Drugtakers in an English Town.* London: Tavistock.

____(1977) Occupational Factors in Industry. In, Grant, M. and Kenyon, W.H. (eds) *Alcoholism and Industry.* London: Alcohol Education Centre/Merseyside, Lancashire and Cheshire Council on Alcoholism, 28-33.

____(1977) Alcoholism and Occupation: A Review. *British Journal of Addiction* 72 (4) December: 309-16.

____(1978) Alcoholism and Occupation: Cause or Effect? A Controlled Study of Recruits to the Drink Trade. *International Journal of the Addictions* 13 (3): 605-626.

Plant, M.A. and Miller, T.I. (1977) Disguised and Undisguised Questionnaires Compared: Two Alternative Approaches to Drinking Behaviour Surveys. *Social Psychiatry* 12: 21-4.

Plant, M.A., Miller, T.I., Kreitman, N., and Duffy, J. (1977) Observing Public Drinking. *Journal of Studies on Alcohol* 38 (5) May: 867-80.

Plant, M.A. and Pirie, F. (1979) Self-Reported Alcohol Consumption and Alcohol-Related Problems: A Study in Four Scottish Towns. *Social Psychiatry.*

Popham, R.E. (1970) Indirect Methods of Alcoholism Prevalence Estimation: A Critical Evaluation. In, Popham, R.E. (ed.) *Alcohol and Alcoholism.* Toronto: Toronto University Press.

Powdermaker, F. (1944-5) Review of Cases at Merchant Marine Rest Centres. *American Journal of Psychiatry* 10: 650-54.

Pursch, J.A. (1976) From Quonset Hut to Naval Hospital. The Story of an Alcoholism Rehabilitation Service. *Journal of Studies on Alcohol* 37 (11): 1655-65.

Rardin, D.R., Lawson, T.R., and Kruzich, D.J. (1974) Opiates, Amphetamines, Alcohol: A Comparative Study of American Soldiers. *International Journal of the Addictions* 9 (6): 891-98.

Registrar General's Decennial Supplement (1971) *Occupational Mortality Tables* (England and Wales). London: HMSO.

Rix, K.J.B. (1975) James Boswell. *Journal of Alcoholism* 10 (2): 73-7.

___(1978)Drinking, Gambling and Wenching. Another View of Bozzy. Personal communication.

Rix, K.J.B., Hunter, D., and Olley, P.C. (1977) Alcoholism and the Fishing Industry in North East Scotland. Paper presented at 3rd Scottish Alcoholism Research Symposium, Loch Achray, April 28.

Robinson, D. (1976) *From Drinking to Alcoholism. A Sociological Commentary*. London: Wiley.

Roman, R.M. and Trice, H.M. (1970) The Development of Deviant Drinking: Occupational Risk Factors. *Archives of Environmental Health* 2: 424-35.

___(1972) Deviance and Work: The Influence of Alcohol and Drugs on Job Behaviours. *Reviews on Environmental Health* 1 (1): 9-51.

Rose, H.K. and Glatt, M.M. (1961) A Study of Alcoholism as an Occupational Hazard of Merchant Seamen. *Journal of Mental Science* 107: 18-30.

Royal College of Psychiatrists (1979) *Alcohol and Alcoholism: The Report of a Special Committee*. London: Tavistock.

Saunders, W. and Kershaw, P. (1977) The Clydebank Community Survey. Paper presented at the 3rd Scottish Alcoholism Research Symposium, Loch Achray, April 27.

Schilling, R.S.F. (1966) Trawler Fishing: An Extreme Occupation. *Proceedings of the Royal Society of Medicine* 59: 405-10.

Schmidt, D.W. (1972) Analysis of Alcohol Consumption Data. The Use of Consumption Data for Research Purposes. *Report on Conference on Epidemiology of Drug Dependence*. London: World Health Organization.

Schramm, C.J. (ed.) (1977) *Alcoholism and its Treatment in Industry*. Baltimore: Johns Hopkins University Press.

Schukit, M.A. and Gunderson, E.K.E. (1974) The Association Between Alcoholism and Job Type in the United States Navy. *Quarterly Journal of Studies on Alcohol* 35: 577-85.

_____(1974) Alcoholism Among Navy and Marine Corps Officers. *Military Medicine* 139: 809-11.

Sclare, A.B. (1978) Alcohol Abuse in the Armed Services. Paper presented at the 2nd International Conference on Psychological Stress and Adjustment in Time of War and Peace, Jerusalem, Israel, June.

Scott, G. and Pottle, F.A. (eds) (1932) *The Private Papers of James Boswell,* 18 vols. Privately printed.

Smart, R.G. (1976) *The New Drinkers: Teenage Use and Abuse of Alcohol.* Ontario: Addiction Research Foundation.

_____(1978) Characteristics of Alcoholics Who Drink Socially After Treatment. *Alcoholism: Clinical and Experimental Research* 2 (1): 39-52.

Sommer, R. (1965) The Isolated Drinker in the Edmonton Beer Parlor. *Quarterly Journal of Studies on Alcohol* 26: 95-110.

Spratley, T.A. (1969) Occupation as a Cause of Alcoholism, M.Phil. Dissertation, University of London.

Stengel, I. (1964) *Suicide and Attempted Suicide.* Harmondsworth: Penguin.

Stimson, G.V., Oppenheimer, E., and Thorley, A. (1978) Seven Year Follow-Up of Heroin Addicts: Drug Use and Outcome. *British Medical Journal* 1(6121): 1190-92.

Straus, R. and Winterbottom, M.T. (1949) Drinking Patterns in an Occupational Group: Domestic Servants. *Quarterly Journal of Studies on Alcohol* 10: 441-60.

Strayer, R. (1957) A Study of Employment and Adjustment of 80 Male Alcoholics. *Quarterly Journal of Studies on Alcohol* 18: 278-87.

Talbott, G.D., Shoemaker, K.E., Follo, M.L., and Bullard, A.L. (1976) Some Dynamics of Addiction Among Physicians. *Journal of the Medical Association of Georgia* 65 March: 77-83.

Thomas, C.B. (1976) What Becomes of Medical Students: The Dark Side. *Johns Hopkins Medical Journal* 138: 185-95.

Trice, H.M. and Roman, P.M. (1972) *Spirits and Demons at Work: Alcohol and Other Drugs on the Job.* Ithaca: New York State School of Industrial and Labor Relations, Cornell University.

Tunstall, J. (1962) *The Fishermen.* St Albans: MacGibbon and Kee.

United States Navy Enlisted Occupational Handbook (1963). Washington: Department of Naval Personnel.

United States Office of Vital Statistics (1961) *Mortality in 1950 by Occupation and Industry*, Special Reports No. 53 Washington DC.

Wallinga, J.V. (1956) Severe Alcoholism in Career Military Personnel. *United States Armed Forces Medical Journal* 7: 551-61.

Wilkins, R.H. (1972) A Survey of Abnormal Drinkers in a General Practice. Paper presented at 30th International Congress on Alcoholism and Drug Dependence, Amsterdam, September.

——(1974) *The Hidden Alcoholic in General Practice*. London: Elek.

Willis, J. (1973) *Addicts: Drugs and Alcohol Re-Examined*. London: Pitman.

Wilson, G.B. (1940) *Alcohol and the Nation*. London: Nicholson and Watson.

World Health Organization (1951) Expert Committee on Mental Health *Alcoholism Subcommittee Second Report*. Geneva WHO, Technical Report Series No. 48.

——(1957) Expert Committee on Mental Health *Report on Fifth Session of Alcoholism Subcommittee*. Geneva: WHO, Technica Report Series No. 42.

Name index

Hewitt, L.E., *24, 39*
Hitz, D., *37*
Hochwald, H., *38*
Hood, R., *44*
Hore, B.D., *14, 29-30, 131*
Hughes, J.P.W., *39*
Hunter, D., *21*

Irgens-Jensen, O., *19, 39, 40*

J.I.F., *18, 39*
Jahoda, G., *6, 133*
Jellinek, E.M., *41*

Keevil, J.J., *19*
Keller, M., *11*
Kenyon, W.H., *132*
Kershaw, P., *43*
Kessel, N., *4, 12-14, 67*
Kessler, M., *45*
Klotter, J., *23*
Kolb, D., *19-21, 38, 39*
Krasner, N., *13*
Kreitman, N., *15, 42, 45, 68*

Lawes, T.G.G., *28-29, 30, 39*
Ledermann, S., *41*
Leodolter, I., *27, 38*
Lemere, F., *28, 30*
Lint, J. de, *43*
Litin, E.M., *26*
Lloyd, R.W., *135*
Long, J.R., *24, 39*
Ludlam, J.E., *25*

McLauchlan, I.E.J., *26*
Makela, K., *10*
Maletsky, B.M., *23*
Maxwell, M.A., *28, 30*
Mayer, J., *29-30*
Mellor, C.S., *37*
Merseyside Council on Alcoholism, *30*
Miller, T.I., *45*
Miller, W., *135*
Moser, J., *11*
Muñoz, R., *135*
Murray, P., *22*
Murray, R.M., *25-26, 39*
Myerson, D.J., *29-30*

Noie, N., *25*

O'Connor, J., *7-8, 10*
O'Hollaren, P., *28, 30*

Office of Population Censuses and
   Surveys, *30-34, 40*
Olley, P.C., *21*
Oppenheimer, E., *130*

Pattison, E.M., *135*
Pernanen, K., *42*
Peto, J., *44*
Pirie, F., *5, 10, 36, 42, 59*
Pittman, D.J., *8-9*
Plant, M.A., *5, 10, 29, 36, 37, 42, 43,
   45, 48, 59*
Polich, J.M., *135*
Popham, R.E., *42*
Pottle, F.A., *22*
Powdermaker, F., *18*
Price, A.C., *23*

Quinton, D., *88*

Registrar General, *30-34*
Rix, K.J.B., *21, 22*
Room, R., *10, 11, 35, 66, 121*
Roman, R.M., *23, 37, 39, 40*
Rose, H.K., *18-19, 39, 40*
Royal College of Psychiatrists, *1*
Rutter, M., *88*

Salzberg, H.C., *135*
Saunders, W., *43*
Schmidt, W., *42, 43*
Schramm, C.J., *14, 132*
Schukit, M.A., *19*
Sclare, A.B., *23*
Scott, G., *22*
Scott, Sir W., *22*
Scottish Health Education Unit, *137*
Shaw, S., *43*
Shoemaker, K.E., *25, 40*
Smart, R.G., *6, 135*
Smith, E., *29-30*
Sommer, R., *45*
Sparks, R., *44*
Spratley, T.A., *29, 30, 43*
Stacey, B., *6-7, 15, 133, 136*
Stambull, H.B., *135*
Stengel, I., *15*
Stimson, G.V., *130*
Storm, T., *6-7, 45*
Straus, R., *22, 39*
Strayer, R., *38*

Talbott, G.D., *25, 40*
Thomas, C.B., *26*

Subject index

absenteeism, 14, 78, 102, 116, 131-32
accidents, 131
addiction (see dependence)
advertising, 11
age, of respondents, 52, 72, 80, 85, 87,
    94, 104, 113
    of partner, 67-68
aims of the study, 46
affluence, 28, 35, 39
alcohol, description, 2-5
    production, 27, 31-34, 38, 39, 47-49
alcoholics, in agencies, 28-30
    in study, 69, 86, 94, 103, 113, 117,
    120-21, 131
alcoholism, definition, 11-15
amended interview schedule, 49, 146-49
amnesias, 13-14, 86
armed forces, 18-24, 29, 31, 39, 40, 66
assessment of drinking, 48, 58-59, 75,
    83, 97, 108, 114-15
attempted suicide (see parasuicide)
availability, 19, 27, 32, 59-60, 69, 71,
    133-34
average consumption (see drinking
    patterns)

boredom, 106-7, 134
brewers, 27, 31-35, 38-39

Camba, 9
cannabis, 1, 78, 84, 87

children, 5-8
coca, 1
clinical records, 28-30
collusion, 23, 40
commercial travellers, 28, 38-39
company directors, 23, 29, 31-32, 39, 40
conclusions, 128-37
controlled drinking, 135
convictions, 65-66, 78, 84-85, 87, 102,
    111, 116, 136
crime, 15

death, the, 91, 92, 122-23
delirium tremens, 13, 117
dependence, 4, 12-13
design of study, 48-50
discussion, 128-38
distillers, 47
divorce, 52, 78, 85, 102, 111-12, 116
doctors, 17, 24-27, 31-34, 39-40
domestic servants, 22, 39
drinking, determinants of, 5-11, 132-37
    patterns, 54-58, 72-75, 80-83, 85-86,
    94-97, 104-8, 113-14
    problems, 11-15, 62-66, 76-78,
    83-85, 100-2, 109-12, 115-17
    at work, 59-60, 76, 86, 93, 97-98,
    108-9, 115, 133-34, 137
drunkenness, 6, 15, 61, 76, 79, 86, 93,
    98-99, 109, 115, 131-33, 134, 137
drugs, 1-2, 25, 26, 87